MW01014801

Controlling Design Variants:
Modular Product Platforms

Controlling Design Variants:
Modular Product Platforms

By Anna Ericsson and
Gunnar Erixon, Ph.D.

Society of Manufacturing Engineers
Dearborn, Michigan

Copyright © 1999 by Modular Management AB and Society of Manufacturing Engineers

987654321

All rights reserved, including those of translation. This book, or parts thereof, may not be reproduced by any means, including photocopying, recording or microfilming, or by any information storage and retrieval system, without permission in writing of the copyright owners.

No liability is assumed by the publisher with respect to use of information contained herein. While every precaution has been taken in the preparation of this book, the publisher assumes no responsibility for errors or omissions. Publication of any data in this book does not constitute a recommendation or endorsement of any patent, proprietary right, or product that may be involved.

Library of Congress Catalog Card Number: 99-072806
International Standard Book Number: 0-87263-514-7

Additional copies may be obtained by contacting:

Society of Manufacturing Engineers
Customer Service
One SME Drive, P.O. Box 930
Dearborn, Michigan 48121
1-800-733-4763
www.sme.org

SME staff who participated in producing this book:

Millicent Treloar, Senior Editor
Rosemary Csizmadia, Production Supervisor
Frances Kania, Production Assistant
Kathye Quirk, Production Assistant/Cover Design

Cover photo: Christoph Eshenbach conducting the Houston Symphony, 1989. Photographer: Crossley and Pogue

Printed in the United States of America

Acknowledgements

The authors want to thank the many people who encouraged, helped, and advised us to write this book: Our colleagues at Modular Management AB for sharing their experiences and wisdom, especially Arne Erlandsson, Alex von Yxkull, and Johan Fredrikson; and The Swedish Institute for Production Engineering Research, Department of Manufacturing Systems, at the Royal Institute of Technology in Stockholm, and Dalarna University for valuable contributions and for sharing research results.

About the Authors

Anna Ericsson and Dr. Gunnar Erixon are consultants in product development with Modular Management AB, Stockholm, Sweden. You may contact them with questions at *www.modular-management.se*.

Anna Ericsson has a MSc degree in mechanical engineering from The Royal Institute of Technology in Stockholm, Sweden. Part of her engineering studies were also performed at Ecole Nationale Supérieure des Mines de Nancy, France. In 1997, she joined Modular Management AB and is today project manager. She has vast experience from working on product development projects within industrial equipment, power transmission, construction equipment, and telecommunications companies.

Dr. Erixon is a Senior Lecturer at Dalarna University in Sweden. He completed his Ph.D. in engineering in 1998 at the Royal Institute of Technology, Stockholm, Sweden. Much of the material in this book is drawn from research performed in completion of his doctoral thesis. With more than 20 years experience at different Swedish companies, Dr. Erixon became one of the co-founders of Modular Management AB in 1996. In 1994, he received the Alde Nilsson ABB Prize for production engineering research contribution, and in 1999, the Karlebo Prize for the work behind his doctoral thesis.

Table of Contents

Preface

An increasing number of successful manufacturing companies such as Sony, Nippondenso, Volvo, Scania, Volkswagen, and Xerox use the notions of modules and product platforms. But, what is a module and how can modular product platforms increase company efficiency while reducing time to market?

A *module*, most simply, is a building block with defined interfaces. The complete set of modules, the *platform*, forms a common structure from which a stream of derivative products can be efficiently developed, marketed, and produced. Using a modular product platform design approach, many variations of final products can be built while controlling the internal complexity that often besets manufacturing companies as they increase customer choices of product design features.

In this book, we describe the driving forces behind modular design and how it can help companies shorten developmental lead times, manage a high degree of customization, and reinforce product identity. We also present a systematic method to incorporate modular design principles into product development. The method is exemplified with case studies from Volvo Car Corporation, Atlas Copco Controls AB, VBG Produkter AB, VBG Ltd., and Sepson AB.

Our intention has been to write a book dealing with the early phases of product development, specifically with the creation of modular product platforms. Our purpose is to give managers and engineering project leaders in product development, design and manufacturing, or anyone else concerned with product development, an introduction to the many possibilities and advantages the modular product platform design offers.

Chapter 1 presents a short historical perspective on the changes that have occurred in product and manufacturing complexity during the 20th century. Chapter 2 identifies and discusses the four primary influences on product development leading to the modular concept. These are (1) a customer-driven marketing strategy that results in a high level of required product variance; (2) an intense competitive environment with ever-increasing demands on reducing time to market; (3) the existing base of family and platform product design; and (4) the critical importance of a close relationship between product design and the production system. Chapter 3 introduces the terminology of product modularity. Twelve different Module Drivers™, covering the entire product life cycle, are identified. Chapter 4 describes how the drivers can be used to systematically create a modular product, reflecting a company's specific needs. In Chapter 5, the steps and tools of the method are clarified with a fictitious example, a vacuum cleaner.

Chapter 6 presents how Volvo, Atlas Copco, VBG, and Sepson have used the method and the results they have achieved. The Volvo case clarifies how a large corporation can use modular design to manage extensive projects, while the VBG case describes how the product design and production systems can be effectively coupled. The Atlas Copco case, together with the Sepson case, illustrates how modularity supports short-development lead times and efficient product variant handling.

Chapter 7 discusses how company strategy and product development can be linked, how product development can be efficiently and rapidly performed, how customization and numerous product variants can be handled, how systematic working methods support the organization, and how small factories within the factory can be created. An appendix contains an extensive derivation of parameters for evaluating modular concepts.

Introduction

Throughout the 20th century, market complexity has increased considerably. In the late 1990s, most companies are forced to concentrate on ever more specific market segments and constantly strive for shorter development lead times. With market complexity has followed a high degree of product assortment complexity, resulting in decreased efficiency within companies. The pursuit of customer-specific products has led to ad hoc solutions for product-related activities. As a result, time spent on nonvalue-added operations per product has increased.

Different approaches and tools for improving corporate efficiency have been developed over the years, as shown in Figure 1-1. The Taylorism of the 1920s was aimed at achieving efficient production through scientific management. Company hierarchy was explicit and labor was divided into small tasks. Every employee was given very specific responsibilities. A rational production system was obtained, but other issues, such as work satisfaction and holistic understanding of the product, were completely disregarded.

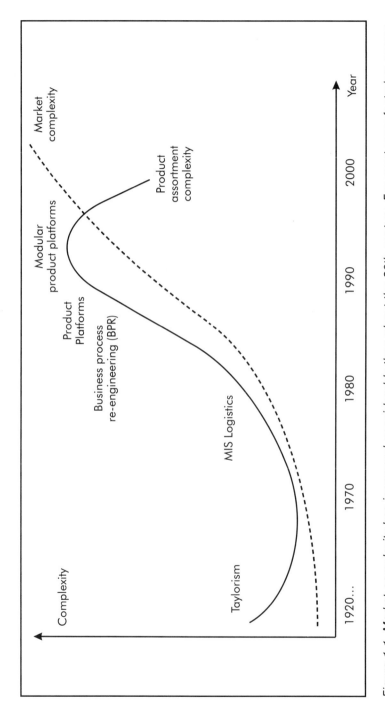

Figure 1-1. Market complexity has increased considerably throughout the 20th century. For most manufacturing compa- nies, this has lead to a growing number of product variants and increased product assortment complexity. When the product assortment complexity grows, corporate efficiency tends to decrease. With the introduction of modular products in the 1990s, companies have a unique possibility to regain control of efficiency in product-related activities.

Much later, during the 1970s, newly emerging information technology moved the corporate focus to management information systems and logistics. By implementing huge, advanced information-handling systems, companies sought efficiency in material and production control. These systems, however, proved to be rigid and did not solve organization-related problems. In the 1980s, the need for organizational agility led to the development of *business process re-engineering* (BPR). BPR implies redesigning the company's processes to obtain improvements in cost, quality, service, speed, and so on.

Streamlining the organization cuts costs, but it has become evident that any measure to considerably improve corporate efficiency must start out from the heart of the company—the product. Most manufacturing companies have experienced an explosion of product variants since the late 1980s. For example, there are companies with a yearly production of only a few thousand product units comprised of 15 basic models containing 20 or more variants in each. Typically, there has just never been enough time to rationalize the entire range of products. Instead, customer needs have been met with ad hoc solutions and, in many cases, specially built products.

During the 1980s, automation stood out as a solution to some of the resulting problems occurring in the production system, such as long lead-times, quality problems due to difficult assembly operations, monotonous work, bad ergonomics, and heavy administration due to many part numbers. However, many companies learned the hard way that automation itself does not solve all problems; it just automates the production process—good or bad. Multiple part numbers complicated material handling. Automatic feeders can rarely handle more than a few different kinds of parts and, since they are often rather space demanding, the layout around automatic assembly lines quickly became a critical issue. Automated systems also proved to be less flexible than corresponding manual ones—a human being

3

can quickly learn to assemble a new product variant, while an automated solution most often demands a certain amount of developmental effort. Heavy investments in automated equipment made companies hesitant to consider continuous development of the product design. The positive effects of automation on production lead-time and quality were obtained only for products, or parts of products, with limited variety. Too many variants led to the situation of changeover time swallowing the effects of speeded-up assembly and, in general, improved quality was obtained only after a period of process and equipment trimming.

When product assortment complexity grows, design considerations tend to focus on lower component levels than on building an optimal product assortment. For example, an automaker wanted to offer customers the option of a CD player. The CD designer, however, did not consider other parts of the vehicle. So, when the cars were eventually built, cars with CD players required a different dashboard assembly than cars without. The lack of a well-defined product structure with specified interfaces may, as in this example, result in variety spreading throughout the product in most unfortunate ways. As product assortment complexity grows and commonality between products decreases, the potential effects of synergy and coordination within the product assortment are lost.

As the manufacturing industry heads into the 21st century, companies have started thinking in terms of product platforms with the main objective of shortening development lead times and increasing commonality between products. The aim is, of course, cost reduction in development and production. However, a risk with product platforms has turned out to be that the products may loose their identity—their profile. This may compromise the brand image and result in decreasing sales volumes.

Profitability is not only about cutting costs—it is also about increasing revenues. With a modular product platform structure, a set of building blocks (modules) is created with which, through different combinations, a great number of final products can be built. Parts of the product that strategically should vary to satisfy customer needs are well defined and separated from the parts of the product that should be kept as common units. In this way, many variants of final products can be handled without increasing a company's internal complexity. This might be referred to as "mass customization."

By breaking a complex product structure into smaller, manageable units, a company can regain control of the product and the product-related activities. The Scania Truck Cab, shown in Figure 1-2, is an excellent example. By modularizing the cab, Scania can offer their customers a wider range of products than previously, requiring fewer parts, less pressing tools, and shorter assembly time.

Instead of searching for an optimal design for an optimal product, the objective of a modular product platform is to create a strategically flexible product design that allows product variations without requiring changes in the overall product design every time a new product variant is introduced. By creating an agile product structure, market and technology changes can be handled more easily. This helps a company take control of development without losing innovation initiative. A well-thought-out modular product architecture will limit the impact of changes and make them manageable.

Modularity aims at increasing efficiency by reducing complexity. The modular approach implies building an optimal product assortment that takes into consideration development, design, variety, manufacture, quality, purchase, and after-sales service, in other words, the entire product life-cycle. A cornerstone of modularity is the adoption of a common view of the product throughout the entire organization. Unlike other approaches discussed earlier, modularity avoids focusing on certain areas without considering

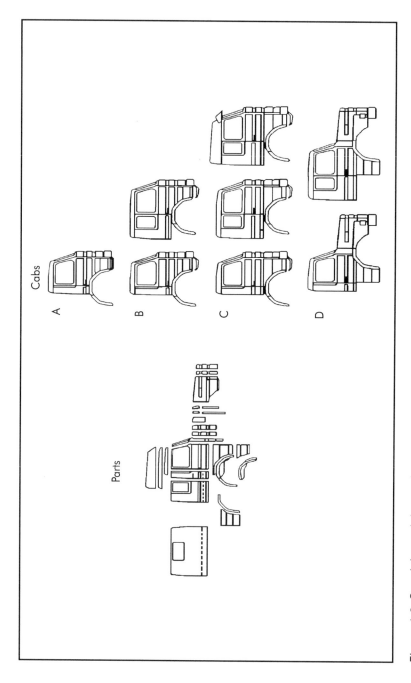

Figure 1-2. Scania's modular truck cab. With the modularized cab, Scania can offer their customers a wider range of products than previously and they now have fewer parts, fewer pressing tools, and shorter assembly time.

others. Automation, for instance, focuses only on production. This is a very important part of the product's life but, for maximum corporate efficiency, the entire product lifecycle needs to be considered. The product platform philosophy mainly concentrates on rationalization by identifying parts or subsystems of the products that should be kept as common units. This approach might, as discussed earlier, have negative effects on the product identity. In the modular approach, which aims at cost reduction simultaneously with increased market shares, it is just as important to identify the parts of the product that *should* vary between different market segments and those that carry the product identity. In this way, a balance between cost-cutting measures and options for increasing market shares can be established.

With the broad overview that a good modular product structure offers, the company can regain control of product assortment. Development resources can be focused to strategically important areas. A large variety of final products can be handled with a limited number of parts. A rational production system with low stock levels and short lead-times can be obtained along with increased commonality between products, fewer part numbers, and greater use of parallel activities. Quality improvements and shorter feedback links can be realized by testing subsystems before final assembly. Closer cooperation with a smaller number of vendors is facilitated by the possibility of outsourcing well-defined subsystems. The after-sales service market shares can be enlarged by offering intelligently shaped service parts and upgrading possibilities.

The product is the heart of the company. Therefore, the company's strategy and visions should be reflected in the product. The product development plan should support the entire organization in working toward the same goal.

7

The essence of a modular product platform is a stream of products in line with company strategy, built from a common structure, consisting of a set of modules and interfaces. It produces company-specific deliverables that can be efficiently developed, marketed, and produced, depending upon the company's objectives.

Expanding and Deviating Demands on Product Design

Today's marketplace reality is characterized by rapid, uncertain, and continuous change. New markets and products constantly arise, change, and disappear within shorter and shorter periods of time. Competition forces companies to concentrate on ever more specific market segments with a rapidly growing product range as a result. These circumstances create complex problems that are difficult to oversee and holistically manage. The internal complexity is a fact.

EXPLOSION OF VARIANTS

Increasingly demanding customers make a high degree of market adaptation and market orientation necessary. Competition forces companies to concentrate on ever smaller market segments, sometimes becoming even customer specific. Most manufacturing companies experienced a formal explosion of product variants in the late 1980s. Figure 2-1 shows an example from BMW (Warnecke 1993).

Widespread product variety is often, besides customer requirements, driven by the product design and the design engineers themselves. Dependencies and functional couplings within the product design may cause design modifications to spread widely within a product. A small, customer-driven design change may have an impact on parts within the product where a modification is of no interest at all to the customer.

Many design engineers find it difficult to search for design solutions already used in predecessor products. Although many companies have implemented heavy support systems, it may be more time-saving to create new parts than to search for already existing ones. A contributing

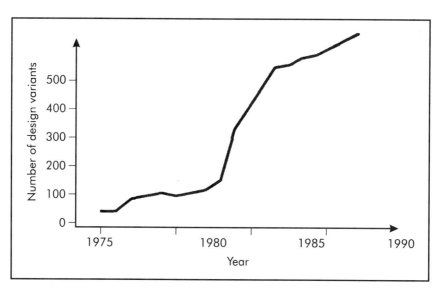

Figure 2-1. The development of the number of car variants at BMW from 1975 to the early 1990s. Like most manufacturing companies, BMW experienced a formal explosion of product variants in the late 1980s.

factor also may be that reward systems for design engineers seem to value creative new solutions higher than the reuse of old ideas.

The creation of product variants tends to increase continually, often unnoticed, until the first problems occur. Too often, these problems lead to quick fixes, but no long-term solutions. The creation of new variants carries on and difficulties start spreading widely within the company.

An uncontrolled variance spoils the possibilities of gaining volume effects in production and, therefore, the possibilities for automation. Numerous parts in the material requirements planning (MRP) system make production planning difficult and will eventually cause inefficient production, but they also complicate logistics and spare parts management.

The costs generated by product variance are often underestimated since they are difficult to capture. Even more difficult to capture is the real revenue increase obtained when introducing yet another variant. People making decisions about introducing variety are often unaware of the impact of their decisions.

TIME

Time to market has become one of the most important elements in competition. For many products, lead times in development have been reduced to half of what they were only a few years ago. Today, for instance, cars are developed in 2–3 years instead of the earlier 4–5 years.

Speeding up the development process means acquiring the flexibility to respond more quickly to new product opportunities. Being among the first companies to bring a new product to market is often the most successful way of gaining a market-leading position. Short lead times in product development also increase the precision in delivering what the customer asks for. The earlier the product is launched after the need has been identified, the larger the market share and the longer the product sales life, as shown in Figure 2-2.

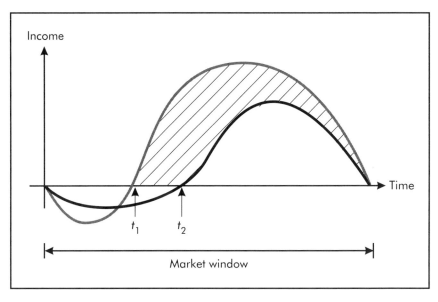

Figure 2-2. Early introduction of a product increases its sales life and market share (Smith and Reinertsen 1991).

The effects of *not* launching products on time has been shown by McKinsey & Co., Inc. (Charney 1991) for a high-tech product. A 6-month delay in product introduction resulted in 33% less profit over 5 years, while an on-time introduction with 50% development expense overrun, resulted in only 4% less profit over the same period.

Product development projects are often considered hard to plan. Most often, targeted project times are overrun and budgeted costs are not met. The uncertainty of these projects often emanates from the desire to create a revolutionary "do everything" product. This often means products containing a high degree of new technology, with which the company has had no experience.

Too often, old products are kept alive as long as possible. Then, suddenly, the product is not competitive anymore and a brand new range of products have to be developed immediately. This makes product development an ad hoc process showing quantum leaps rather than a continuous, planned activity.

DESIGN SCOPE

Today, the scope of a product design project has to be wider than it has been traditionally. The introduction of product platforms implies that the project scope should encompass not a single product, but a family or an assortment of products. Instead of searching for "an optimal design for an optimal product" the objective should be to create a strategically flexible product design, allowing product variations without requiring changes in the overall product design every time a new variant is introduced.

When acting in a competitive market, it is not enough to fulfill the customer requirements concerning functionality and cost. The design project has to consider the product's entire life cycle, including demands on efficiency in future development, production, service, logistics, sales, and recycling. Among the product properties, the identification of "order winners" is also crucial for a successful product design. The "it" within the product—the something that will make the customer choose the product before all other ones—must be identified and carefully guarded.

It is the product architecture that determines how the product can be changed to fit the amount of varying requirements occurring during its lifetime. Therefore, a product development procedure must, from the beginning, consider the product's entire life cycle as well as the product's role in the total assortment.

DESIGN AND MANUFACTURE

It seems obvious that product design strongly influences the design of the production system. However, surprisingly few companies structure and design products in a production-friendly way.

Many independent investigations have shown that the larger portion of a product's production costs is already determined in the design and development phases. Figures ranging from 70–80% or even 90% are often mentioned. However, there is no real evidence in this matter, and it is clear that the influence will vary depending on the type of product considered.

The awareness of the product design's impact on production costs has led to the development of design for manufacture and assembly (DFMA) methods with the objective to aid in designing products for easier production. DFMA methods have been successfully applied in industry and have resulted in widespread improvements in product quality and profitability.

Design for assembly (DFA) rests on the hypothesis that through improvements of the "assemblability" of products, improvements in many other processes automatically follow. When the product arrives at assembly, work-in-progress values are high, time limits are consumed, and earlier neglects, such as incorrect tolerances, bad planning (components missing), and fabrication failures show up. Assembly activities are often labor intensive and must be rationalized. Several activities are involved in assembly, such as transport, handling, insertion, fitting, joining, and control, which makes it a highly integrated process. Adapting the design for assembly process is, therefore, a sound basis for developing products that are easy to manufacture. The most widespread and used method of this type is the Boothroyd and Dewhurst DFA analysis (Boothroyd and Dewhurst 1987).

DFMA applied on a single product, however, is no longer sufficient, because it will result in an optimal design for that specific variant, but not necessarily for other variants within the assortment. This shortcoming of the DFMA methods will be increasingly evident as the previously discussed explosion of variants continues. If the overall product architecture has not been previously defined, there is an obvious risk of suboptimizations.

three

Product Modularity

The product structure, or architecture, is the key to handling complexity. By breaking a complex structure into smaller, manageable units, companies can regain control of the product and product-related activities. Good product architecture can be achieved with modularity.

Product architecture can be treated on three levels: the product range level, product level, and component level. Measures to reduce complexity affect the product range, product, and component levels exponentially as shown in Figure 3-1. There is, therefore, a great potential for improvement if the right design decisions are made at the higher levels.

The development of modular product designs results in many positive effects on the product range level. A properly used modularization has the following advantages:

- higher flexibility—product changes, due to market or new technology, can be made more easily since they will only influence limited parts of the product;
- reduction of product development lead time—parallel development activities are possible once the interfaces between the modules have been defined;

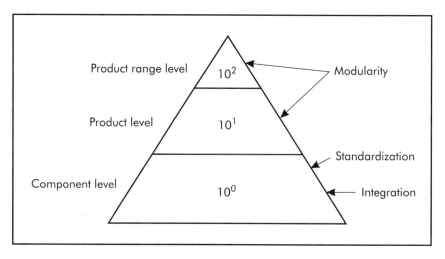

Figure 3-1. Product architecture can be treated on three levels: the product range level, product level, and component level. Measures to reduce complexity affect the levels exponentially.

- parallel development of the product and production system—product development plans can be translated into production plans for each module;
- reduction of production lead time—parallel manufacturing of modules instead of manufacturing an entire product in a single sequence;
- less capital tied up in production—work-in-progress is reduced due to shortened lead times, less stock maintenance of ready-made products;
- reduced material and purchase costs—the reduction of part numbers means less to purchase and less to administrate, and higher volumes per part number;
- improved quality—modules tested before final assembly have shorter feedback links, allowing easier adjustments;
- easier service and upgrading—standardized interfaces make adding or replacing a module easy; and
- easier administration—quoting, planning, and designing customized products can be done more efficiently.

The effects obtained will depend on how the modularization concept is used. Corporate management must define what is expected to provide a guide for the modularized product structure.

<hr>

WHAT IS PRODUCT MODULARITY?

The terms *module, modularization, modularity,* and *modular design* are well known in industry and academia. However, it is difficult to find discrete and unambiguous definitions of these terms.

In an encyclopaedia, the term *module* is defined as "a standardized unit; a combinable, changeable part or component; a class of numbers; any in a series of standardized units for use together; a usually packaged functional assembly of electronic components for use with other such assemblies . . ."

In this book, product modularity is defined as having two characteristics: 1) similarity between the physical and functional architecture of the design, and 2) minimization of the degree of interaction between physical components. Hence, the modular product platform definition of *modularization* is "decomposition of a product into building blocks (modules) with specified interfaces, driven by company-specific strategies." There are many different ways to modularize a product. This definition implies that two companies manufacturing the same type of product could end up with different modularized product structures, depending on their product strategies.

The difference between a module and a subassembly should be noted. A *subassembly* is often the result of the assembly planning activity. Subassemblies are created because the product design does not permit entire assembly in one flow. The need for many subassemblies may be one of the first indicators of poor product design. A *module,* however, is chosen for specific, corporate strategic reasons and the interfaces should take the ability to be assembled into account. It is often beneficial to subassemble the modules off-line of the final assembly line. Consequently, a subassembly is not necessarily a module, but a module is often a subassembly.

MODULE DRIVERS™

The positive effects of modularization described are, of course, the reasons why companies would want to modularize their products. It is not, however, easy to translate a company's objectives into guidelines for product design. However, a number of driving forces for modularization within the product can be identified. These are called *Module Drivers*.

The Module Drivers have been identified through analysis of a great number of case studies. They are the result of 5 years of research work at The Swedish Institute of Production Engineering Research and The Royal Institute of Technology, Stockholm, Sweden.

The Module Drivers cover the entire life cycle of a product and may be linked to different functions of a company as shown in Table 3-1.

Carryover

A *carryover* is a part or a subsystem of a product that most likely will not be exposed to any design changes during the life of the product platform. The part, therefore, can be carried over from an earlier product generation to a later one.

An example of a carryover module is Volvo's window crank mechanism. A customer does not necessarily choose

Table 3-1. Module Drivers™

Product development and design	Carryover
	Technology evolution
	Planned product changes
Variance	Different specification
	Styling
Production	Common unit
	Process and/or organization
Quality	Separate testing
Purchase	Supplier available
After sales	Service and maintenance
	Upgrading
	Recycling

a car because of the technology in the window crank mechanism. The most important thing is that the mechanism has certain functions and properties. As long as the mechanism fulfills customer and company requirements, it can be carried over to future product generations.

Technology Evolution

Technology evolution refers to parts that are likely to undergo changes as a result of changing customer demands or technology shift. The technology itself can evolve, from mechanical to mechatronic, or new materials might be made available that may not have been previously available.

An example of technology evolution is the arch module in the fifth wheel from VBG Ltd. This module was defined as a development module because of the expected introduction of lubrication-free material, as well as the anticipated use of weight sensors in the future. The fifth wheel case is summarized in Chapter 6.

21

Planned Product Changes

Planned product changes concern parts of the product that the company intends to develop and change. These changes may be carried out to launch new product models, better fulfill certain customer demands, or decrease production costs. The product platform development plan, describing these changes and specifying their launching dates, is a strategic tool. The introduction of consecutive models of the Sony Walkman™ is an example of such a product development plan (see Figure 3-2).

Different Specification

To handle product variation and customization effectively, a designer should strive to allocate all variations to as few product parts as possible. It is also advantageous to make the variation adaptation as late as possible in the production chain to improve inventory savings, customer service, and lower overall costs.

The power unit of the HP DeskJet™ printer is an example of a *different specification* module. The printer is delivered with a different power unit enclosed in the package, depending on the geographic market.

Parameterization of one or a few modules can be an efficient way of handling differences in parameters such as length or volume. Many computer-aided design (CAD) systems have standard routines for parameterization that facilitate product design by information reuse.

Styling

Some parts of a product may be strongly influenced by trends and fashion, or closely connected to a brand or trademark. Therefore, *styling* modules that typically contain visible parts of the product should be used to underline

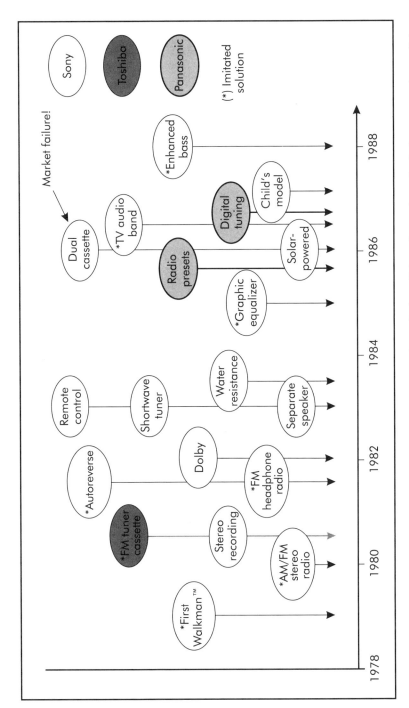

Figure 3-2. The product platform development plan is a strategic tool, describing planned product changes and specifying their launching dates. This plan shows the introduction of consecutive models of the Sony Walkman™.

23

product identity. An example of a styling module is the hood of a vacuum cleaner. Changing the hood color and design can create many different variations of vacuum cleaners.

Common Unit

Although a high degree of customization requires many product variants, it is possible to find parts or subsystems that can be used for the entire product assortment or for large parts of it. Parts carrying functions required by all customers are possible candidates for *common unit* modules.

The difference between a common unit and a carryover should be observed. A carryover implies a long lifetime for the module, while a common unit implies large production volumes. The ideal situation is when these two module drivers can be combined. For instance, the driving mechanism of the Sony Walkman was used in all models of the product (common unit), at the same time as it was carried over through several generations within the product platform (carryover).

Process and/or Organization

To make production as efficient as possible, parts of the product requiring the same specific production process are clustered together. At VBG Ltd. (see Chapter 6), for instance, all parts requiring welding processes were moved to one single module. The welding of this module could then be automated.

Suitable work content, special process skills, manageable ergonomics, and long lead-time processes are all organizational-related reasons for forming a module.

Separate Testing

The possibility of *separately testing* each module before delivery to final assembly may contribute to significant quality improvements. This is mainly due to the reduced feedback times. The complaints and quality loss statistics may be searched if part quality is a concern.

Available from Supplier

Instead of buying individual parts from subcontractors, some subsystems in the product may be suitable for purchase as standard modules from vendors. This black-box engineering implies that the vendor takes the manufacture, development, and quality responsibility (that is, total responsibility). For these modules, a traditional make-or-buy analysis must be carried out and should address these questions:

- are there strategic reasons why the technology should be kept in-house?;
- have we today and in the future enough resources to develop and produce this module?; and
- is there any vendor offering the subsystem as a standard module today?

For example, Hella, a former supplier of only headlights, is today responsible for the delivery of complete car fronts to Volkswagen (for use in their Golf™ product line).

Service and Maintenance

Quick service and maintenance in the field is often an important customer requirement. Therefore, parts exposed to service and maintenance may be clustered together to form a *service* module. With intelligently shaped interfaces, a new module can quickly replace a damaged one. For instance, beneath the passenger compartment of the X2000 (Swedish high-speed train), all electrical wires and hydraulic tubes are assembled in drawer shelf-type boxes. These boxes are pre-assembled and serviced outside the train under more ergonomic working conditions (upright standing at table height instead of up underneath the train).

Upgrading

Designing a module to allow *upgrading* offers customers the possibility of changing the product in the future. For instance, the product can be rebuilt for another purpose or, more often, functions can be added or the product performance improved. A typical example of a product that is designed to allow for upgrading is a personal computer.

Recycling

There is a growing interest in environmental issues and the emphasis on sustainable design increases. This is mainly because of the growing number of environmental regulations and consumer preferences for "green" products. To enable a high degree of recycling, the number of different materials in each module should be limited. Environmentally hostile or easily recyclable material can be kept separate in specific modules so that the disassembly of the product for recycling or disposal will be simplified.

HOW ARE THE MODULE DRIVERS USED?

The Module Drivers form the base in a systematic evaluation of the technical solutions for a given product. To aid the evaluation, a matrix in which every technical solution is assessed against the Module Drivers is used. The procedure will be further described in Chapter 4. The terminology concerning the Module Drivers may vary. For instance, slightly different names for the drivers are used in the cases in Chapter 6 due to differing company cultures. However, the theoretical basis for the Module Drivers rests as described in this chapter.

The theory that increased product modularity gives positive effects in the total flow of information and materials—from development and purchasing to storage and delivery—is supported by many. Researchers and practitioners also advocate product modularity as an excellent base for continuous product renewal and concurrent development of the manufacturing system. What is clear, though, is that very few describe *how* a modular product design can be developed.

four

Modular Function Deployment™

Modular Function Deployment™ (MFD™) is a structured, company-supportive method with the objective of finding the optimal modular product design, taking into consideration the company's specific needs. MFD supports the entire concept phase of the product development process, from product idea to computer-aided design (CAD) drawing. The method is applicable to an entire product range and is most successful when implemented by a cross-functional project team. MFD consists of five major steps, as shown in Figure 4-1.

The first step makes sure that the right design requirements are derived from the customer demands. The properties the product must have to satisfy present and future market demands are defined by analysis of competition and customer requirements.

In the second step, functions that fulfill the demands and their corresponding technical solutions are identified. There might be several technical solutions to fulfill

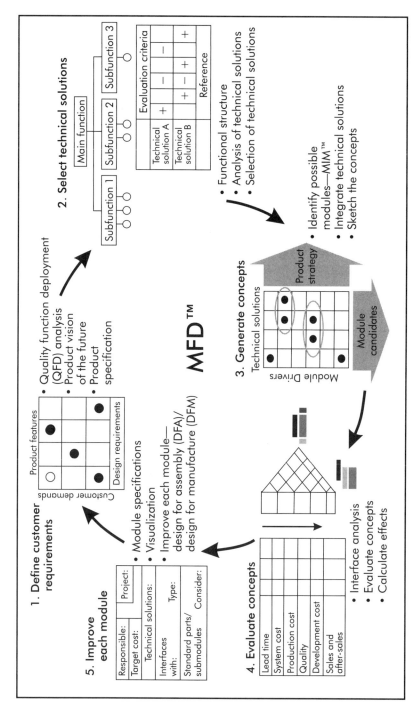

Figure 4-1. The five steps of Modular Function Deployment™. The circle illustrates that design work is an iterative process.

a specific function, but only the most appropriate technical solutions with regard to customer needs and other company-relevant criteria are chosen.

In the third step, the core in the MFD method, the technical solutions are analyzed regarding their reasons for being modules. The results of the first two steps of the MFD method are essential in supporting the decisions made when using the Module Drivers to evaluate the technical solutions.

Module concepts are then generated and the interface relations of the modules derived are evaluated in step four. In addition, economic forecasts are made and the expected effects of the modularization are calculated.

In the final step, a specification is established for each module. The specification contains technical information about the module as well as cost targets, planned development, description of variants, etc. From here on, the modular concept can be improved by focusing separately on each module. Depending on the module's characteristic, tools such as design for manufacture (DFM) and design for assembly (DFA) may be successfully applied.

The presentation of the MFD method follows an ideal working manner from step one to five. However, design work very seldom starts from the first specified step in a method, continues through every single step, in the right order, and ends with the final step. Starting points vary and several iterations might be needed before a satisfying result is reached.

_____ STEP 1: DEFINE CUSTOMER REQUIREMENTS

The first step in any method for product design has to ensure that the appropriate design requirements are derived from the customer/market needs. This implies a thorough understanding of the market situation and customer identity. Before anything else, the product strategy, including brand image, must be defined. Some of the important questions demanding answers are: What is our product vision of the future? What is the profile/image of this product on the market? Who are the most important customers? Who are the most important competitors?

The customer requirements must then be defined so that a specification of the product to be designed can be formulated. A simplified version of the well-known method, quality function deployment (QFD), has turned out to be well adapted for this task. Much has been written about the QFD method and is available in the literature.

Considering the objectives here, the usual QFD matrix is modified by putting "modularity" directly in as the first "how" (design requirement) as shown in Figure 4-2. This is preferable to establish the right "mind-set" of the project team members.

When the most important customer requirements have been identified, they are translated into product properties for the design engineers. The relations between customer requirements and product properties are visualized in the QFD matrix (Figure 4-2). Measurable target values for the product properties are then set up to guide the design engineers' work.

—————— STEP 2: SELECT TECHNICAL SOLUTIONS

The design requirements derived from the first step will have a strong market focus. To proceed with the product design, a more technical view is needed. Looking at the product from a functional point of view does this. Functions and subfunctions that fulfill the requirements from step one are identified and the corresponding technical solutions, or function carriers, are selected. This breaking down of the product into functions and their correspond-

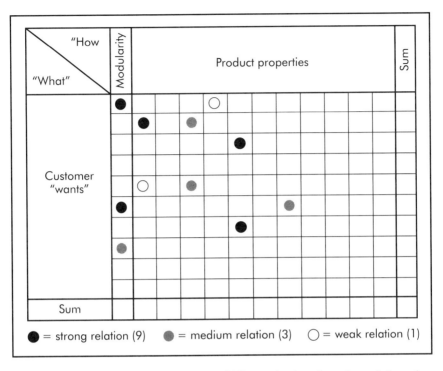

Figure 4-2. A simplified version of the QFD matrix visualizes the relations between customer wants (what) and product properties (how).

ing technical solutions is normally referred to as a *functional decomposition*. Also, by going through the functions for all the parts contained in the product, a mutual understanding of how every part contributes to the whole is achieved within the design team.

A prerequisite to achieving an optimal modular design is functional independence. Functional independence makes it possible to achieve robust modular design where interactions between modules are minimal. The stand-alone modules can then be treated independently from each other.

During the functional decomposition, several technical solutions for a certain function may be found and a choice must be made. Experiences have shown that a matrix is a good way to structure and represent alternative solutions. A Pugh matrix is not a mathematical matrix, but a way to express and clarify the advantages and disadvantages of different options, as shown in Figure 4-3. Evaluation criteria can be collected from step one of the MFD method, together with internal company considerations, such as production goals, part number count, and future development potential.

Technical concepts and solutions	Evaluation criteria										Sum +	Sum −
	Criteria 1	Criteria 2	Criteria 3									
Alternative A	+	−	+	−	+							
Alternative B	+	+	−	−	−							
	Reference											

Figure 4-3. During the functional decomposition of the product, several technical solutions for a certain function may be found and a choice must be made. A Pugh matrix such as this is a good way to structure and represent the advantages and disadvantages of the different alternatives.

Step two will result in a *functions-and-means tree* for the product that visualizes the product's functional structure and selected technical solutions from which the product platform should be built. The top levels of a schematic function-and-means tree are shown in Figure 4-4.

—————— STEP 3: GENERATE MODULE CONCEPT

In the third step, the technical solutions selected in step two are analyzed regarding their reasons for forming modules. The criteria used are the Module Drivers™ described in Chapter 3.

In the Module Indication Matrix™ (MIM™), each technical solution is assessed against the Module Drivers. The

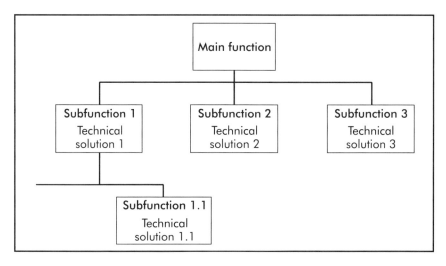

Figure 4-4. In the second step of the MFD method, functions and subfunctions are identified and corresponding technical solutions, or function carriers, are selected. The product's functional structure is visualized in a "functions-and-means" tree.

MIM, shown in Figure 4-5, constitutes the core of the MFD method. Every technical solution is weighted on a scale where nine points correspond to a strong driver, three points a medium driver, and one point a weak driver, according to the importance of its respective reason for being a module. The irregular scaling is used to support the identification of the really strong driving forces.

Many and/or unique module drivers, highly weighted, indicate that the technical solution in question has a complicated requirements pattern and is likely to form a module by itself, or at least, the basis for a module. A unique module driver pattern also indicates that the technical solution should be kept single as long as possible.

Few and/or low weighted module drivers, on the other hand, indicate that the technical solution in question might be easy to encapsulate or group together with other technical solutions. Integration should be executed provided there is a match in the module driver pattern, or at least

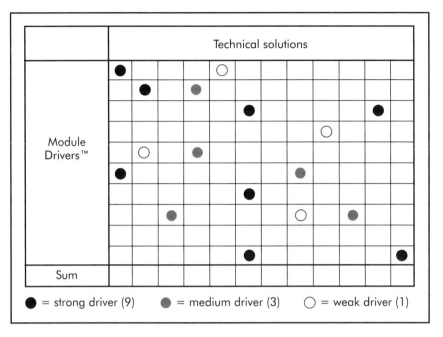

Figure 4-5. In the Module Indication Matrix™, each technical solution is assessed against the Module Drivers™. Every technical solution is weighted on a scale where 9 points = a strong driver, 3 points = a medium driver, and 1 point = a weak driver.

that there are no contradictions. For example, a carryover should not be grouped together with planned product changes because it would disable the possibility to stepwise develop at low cost.

There is an ideal number of modules to look for, in which there is balance between the time required for the assembly of modules and the time required for assembling the finished modules to each other in the main flow. The value is calculated based on the assumption that each module is concurrently assembled with the others and delivered to the main assembly line where complete modules are assembled to each other. Experiences show that an average "best practice" assembly operation time for parts is about 10 seconds and an average final assembly operation between modules varies between 10 and 50 seconds. A rough estimation is therefore that minimum lead time is achieved when the number of modules equals the square root of the number of assembly operations in the average product, as shown in Figure 4-6. When the average final assembly time is longer than the average assembly time for parts, the ideal number of modules will decrease (see the Appendix).

A suitable number of *module candidates*, technical solutions with the highest Module Driver™ scores, are picked out. Then, through pattern recognition in the MIM, lower-weighted technical solutions are evaluated as to the possibility of integration with the module candidates. At this stage, a creativity phase can take place in which a number of different module concepts are proposed. The concepts

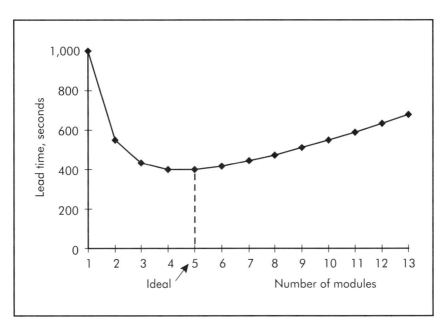

Figure 4-6. Lead time in assembly is a function of the average number of modules in a product. Minimum lead time is achieved when the number of modules equals the square root of the number of assembly operations in the average product.

should contain some rough dimensioning and form. One, or a few, of the concepts are then further worked on.

_____ STEP 4: EVALUATE MODULE CONCEPT

Once a modular concept has been generated, questions arise. What are the effects on production and product development? How much better is the new modular concept compared to the existing design?

For a modular design, the interfaces between modules have a vital influence on the final product and the flexibility within the assortment. So, an examination of the interface relations will be an important part of the evaluation work.

An interface between two modules might be, for example, fixed, moving, or media transmitting. Fixed interfaces only connect modules and transmit forces. Moving interfaces may transmit energy in forms of rotating or alternating forces. Media can be fluids or electricity.

A good overview of the interface relations can be achieved with an interface matrix. The modules are entered in expected assembly order and their interrelations are marked with G for geometry, E for energy transmitting, and so forth. From an assembly point of view, two ideal interface principles can be identified: base unit assembly and "hamburger" assembly. These are marked with arrows in Figure 4-7. It is clear that the two ideal assembly principles are beneficial from many other standpoints besides assembly. They facilitate simultaneous development, provide easier process planning, and allow greater freedom in workshop organization, among other advantages. The matrix serves as a pointer to interfaces that have to be given special attention and, eventually, improved. All markings located outside the arrows indicating the preferred assembly principles should be subject to further consideration.

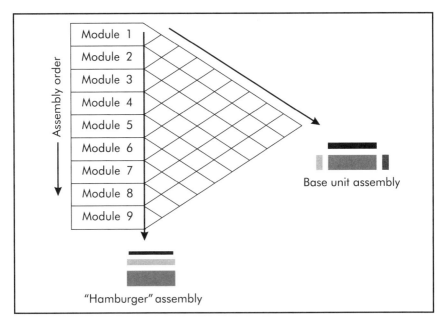

Figure 4-7. For a modular design, the interfaces between modules have a vital influence on the final product and the flexibility within the assortment. A good overview of the interface relations can be achieved with an interface matrix, such as this one, where the modules are entered in expected assembly order and their interrelations are marked with, for instance, G for geometry, E for energy transmitting, etc. From an assembly point of view, two ideal interface principles can be identified: base unit assembly and "hamburger" assembly.

In addition to the interface evaluation, several economic factors must be considered. Normal economic accounting, including activity-based costing (ABC) analysis, does not value all of the advantages and effects that a modular product assortment produces. Also, no existing design for manufacture and assembly (DFMA) method evaluates the advantages on the assortment level. So there is clearly a need for a new evaluation tool.

A rough estimation can be carried out. For some of the effects, a metric or a rule can be defined and used to evaluate the concept (see Table 4-1). The relative importance of the required effects has to be assessed and fixed at the beginning

**Table 4-1. Assigning a metric or rule
to aid in evaluating the effects of modularity**

Effect	Product characteristics	Metric/ rule
Lead time in development	Interface complexity	Metric
Development costs	Share of carryover	Rule
Development capacity	Share of purchased modules	Rule
Product costs	Assortment complexity	Metric
System costs	Share of purchased modules	Rule
Lead time	Number of modules in product	Metric
Quality	Share of separately tested modules	Metric
Variant flexibility	Multiple use	Metric
Service/upgrading	Functional purity in modules	Rule
Recyclability	Material purity in modules	Rule

in every case. The evaluation parameters are further discussed in the Appendix.

During a development process, many choices need to be made and important strategic actions are taken. An evaluation, such as the one shown in Table 4-1, will document such action and serve as feedback to earlier phases in the process.

_____ STEP 5: OPTIMIZE MODULES

In the final step, a specification is written for each module containing technical information, cost targets, planned development, description of variants, etc. The module specifications constitute the backbone of the product platform. From here on, the modular concept can be improved by focusing on each module separately.

The MFD method should not be considered as a replacement for, or competitive with, design improvements on the component level. It is important to emphasize the necessity of such work within every single module to secure the final result. The MIM now serves as a pointer for what is important for each individual module. For instance, a module that is chosen mainly for service and maintenance reasons should be designed for ease of disassembly.

As discussed earlier, product design improvements may take place at different levels: the product range level, product level, and component level. The work on the product and component level has traditionally been extensive and only one aspect will be treated here, namely the number of different parts used to build a product or product range.

The number of different components in a product has been identified to be an important driver of costs in a company. These costs are, however, difficult to capture. Material, labor, and tooling are the most visible costs, but they only represent a part of the total true cost for the company. Many other costs are driven by the part number count and do not show up in traditional calculation systems since they are overhead costs.

In the same way as the number of parts drives costs in a single product, the part numbers drive costs within the entire product assortment. Thus, when using the DFA technique on a single product variant, the entire assortment of products must be taken into account. With a modular product design where the DFMA technique can be applied per module, design improvements on the component level can be carried out with optimal results.

Illustrative Example: Vacuum Cleaner

In this chapter, the MFD™ method will be explained with the help of an illustrative example showing how the method is applied for the modularization of a domestic canister-type vacuum cleaner. The example is a "dummy," but has been partly collaborated on in cooperation with personnel from Electrolux AB. It has also been used at numerous training workshops in modular design.

_____ STEP 1: DEFINE CUSTOMER REQUIREMENTS

As mentioned earlier, the first step in any method for product design must ensure that the appropriate design requirements are derived from the customer needs. Once the company objectives and product strategies have been clarified, the simplified QFD analysis can begin. For the domestic vacuum cleaner, typical customer requirements might be:

43

- high suction performance;
- low price;
- easy to use;
- long working range;
- low noise;
- easy maintenance; and
- easy storage.

From these customer requirements, the corresponding product attributes, or properties, are derived. The product attributes should be parameters that the design engineers can work with. They also should be measurable since target values should be set up for these. Product properties for the vacuum cleaner might be:

- size;
- shape;
- weight;
- noise level;
- range;
- material;
- power; and
- opening force (lid).

The relations between customer demands and product properties are analyzed in the QFD matrix shown in Figure 5-1. The matrix defines what product properties the design engineers can adjust to fulfill a particular customer demand. The relation is graded with a point system where a strong relation is equal to 9 points, a medium relation 3 points, and a weak relation 1 point. The grade is then multiplied with the customer demand weight before it is summarized vertically. Future probable trends for the customer demands are indicated with arrows.

The analysis of different customer segments will yield varying customer demands. This will, in turn, lead to differing target values for the corresponding product properties. For the vacuum cleaner, it might be strategic to offer the customers different sizes, for instance.

Customer requirements	Weight	Trend	Modularization	Size	Shape	Weight	Noise level	Range	Material	Power	Opening force (lid)	Sum
High suction performance	5	↑			1					9		10
Low price	5	←	9						3	9		21
Easy to use	4	↑		9	3	9						21
Long working range	4	←						9				9
Low noise	3	↑					9		3			12
Easy maintenance	3	↑			3						9	12
Easy storage	2	↑		9	3	1						13
Sum:	X	X	45	54	32	38	27	36	24	90	27	

Figure 5-1. QFD matrix for a vacuum cleaner. The matrix defines what product properties the design engineers can adjust to fulfill a particular customer demand. The relations are graded with a point system where a strong relation = 9 points, a medium relation = 3 points and a weak relation = 1 point. The grade is then multiplied with the customer demand weight before it is summarized vertically. Future probable trends for the customer demands are indicated with arrows.

_____ STEP 2: SELECT TECHNICAL SOLUTIONS

The decomposition of a mechanical system is a common activity in engineering design. A functional analysis might be carried out in many different ways, but the main objective is to map all functions, explain them, and put them in their context. To describe the vacuum cleaner's functional structure, some principles from the axiomatic design methodology have been used.

The vacuum cleaner's primary function is to remove dust. To solve that, the technical solution, vacuum nozzle, has been chosen. The vacuum nozzle, in turn, requires these functions: create vacuum, reach every spot, and dispatch dust. To fulfill each of these functions, another three technical solutions are selected, namely fan, mobile chassis, and removable bag. The decomposition is performed down to a practical level. The "nuts and bolts" level is usually too detailed where a good modular structure is the objective. The highest levels of the functional structure for the vacuum cleaner are shown in Figure 5-2.

Technical solutions, or function carriers, on a suitable level in the completed decomposition, are transferred to the Module Indication Matrix™ (MIM™).

_____ STEP 3: GENERATE MODULE CONCEPT

In the Module Indication Matrix, each technical solution is assessed against the Module Drivers™ as explained earlier. The completed MIM for the vacuum cleaner is shown in Figure 5-3.

In the summation of module driver scores shown in Figure 5-4 (taken from the horizontal totals in Figure 5-3), the Module Driver™ profile for the vacuum cleaner shows large totals for common unit and carryover. This

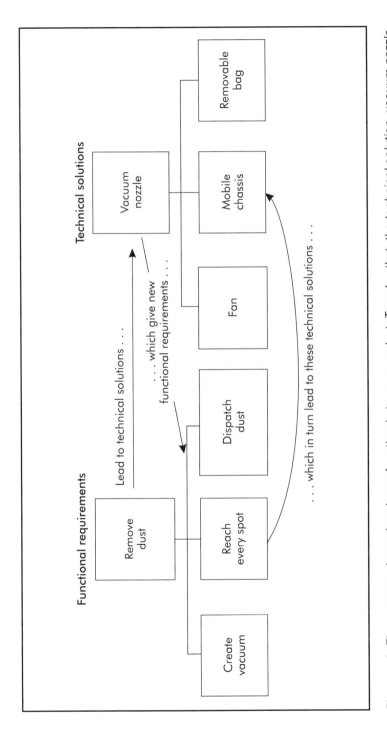

Figure 5-2. The vacuum cleaner's primary function is to remove dust. To solve that, the technical solution, vacuum nozzle, has been chosen. The vacuum nozzle will, in turn, require these functions: create vacuum, reach every spot, and dispatch dust. To fulfill each of these functions, another three technical solutions are selected, namely fan, mobile chassis, and removable bag.

Figure 5-3. In the Module Indication Matrix™, each technical solution is assessed against the Module Drivers™. Module candidates for the vacuum cleaner having the highest scores are filter, electric motor, chassis, bag, thyristor, and fan. Since the battery is a future technical solution, it should not be grouped with any solution from earlier product generations.

● = strong module driver (9 points)   ◉ = medium module driver (3 points)   ○ = weak module driver (1 point)

Module drivers		Fan	Absorbent, fan	Electrical motor	Vibration damper	Absorbent, motor	Chassis	Bag	Filter	Thyristor	Power switch	Cover	Cord and contact	Handle	Rear wheels	Front wheel	Accessories	Bumper	Lid	Indicator	Gasket	O-ring	Cord reel	Bag lock	Manual brake (cord)	Knob, thyristor	Knob, manual brake	Knob, power switch	Battery	Total
Development and design	Carryover	●	◉	◉	◉	◉	●	◉	◉	●	◉	◉	◉	◉	◉	◉	○	◉		●			●	●	◉				●	82
	Technology evolution																													9
	Planned design changes			◉				◉	●			◉	◉	◉					◉											27
Variance	Different specification	○	○	○					○	○			◉													◉				11
	Styling											●		●		●	●	●	●							●				55
Manufacturing	Common unit	◉	◉	◉	●	●	●	●	◉	◉	●	◉	○	◉	◉	●	●	●	●	●	●	●	●	●	●	●	●	●	●	154
	Process/organization			●							○																			18
Quality	Separate testability			●						○																				11
Purchase	Supplier availability							◉	●	●			●										●						○	37
After-sales	Service/maintenance								●	○																			○	23
	Upgrading																													9
	Recycling			●			●					●																	●	36
Total:		22	7	43	12	12	27	27	40	24	13	21	16	12	7	12	10	12	12	18	9	9	27	9	12	12	9	9	29	

48

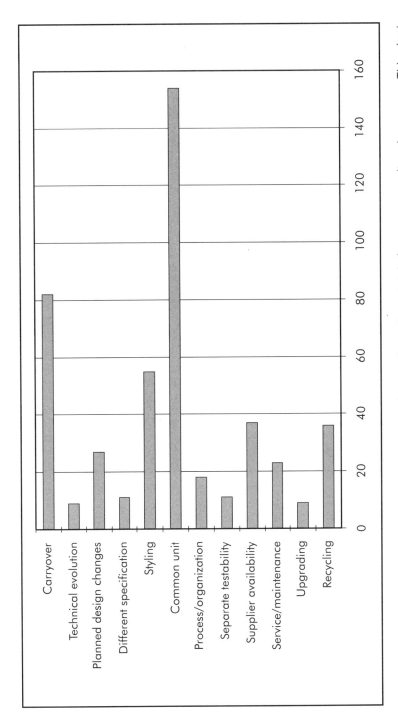

Figure 5-4. The Module Driver profile for the vacuum cleaner shows large totals for common unit and carryover. This signifies a mature product with limited technical development. The strong styling driver indicates that market differentiation is driven by design changes.

signifies a rather mature product with limited technical development. The styling driver is also strong, which signifies that to a great deal market differentiation is realized through design changes.

The number of parts to be assembled for the vacuum cleaner is estimated to be about 70, yielding eight (the nearest square root of 70) as an ideal number of modules. The eight module candidates, that is, the eight technical solutions having the highest Module Driver scores (except battery*) are:

- fan;
- electric motor;
- chassis;
- bag;
- filter;
- thyristor;
- cover; and
- cord reel.

Grouping, or integration, of technical solutions with the module candidates can now be executed. For the vacuum cleaner, the chassis and cover would seem to be a suitable module. However, their Module Driver marks are somewhat conflicting. What differs is the fact that the chassis has a strong driver for a common unit, while the housing has a strong driver for styling. An integration of these two would lead to a need for early fixation of varieties in the production process. However, there could be other reasons for conducting this integration. The most important thing at this point is to open the problem for discussion.

The nine modules finally chosen for the vacuum cleaner are shown in Table 5-1. Some of the technical solutions

---

* Since the battery is a potential future technical solution, it should not be grouped together with any technical solution from earlier product generations.

Table 5-1. Nine modules, their drivers,
and technical solutions for a vacuum cleaner

Module	Most important Module Driver™	Technical solutions
Styling module	Styling	Cover Handle (with integrated bumper) Lid
Panel module	Styling	Knob, thyristor Knob, power switch Knob, manual brake
Electric motor module	Separate testing Common unit	Electric motor Thyristor Power switch
Chassis module	Carryover Common unit	Chassis Rear wheels Front wheel Bag lock Vibration damper Accessories
Bag module	Service/maintenance	Bag
Filter module	Upgrading	Filter
Cord reel module	Supplier available	Cord reel Manual brake
Absorbent module	Supplier available	Absorbent
Fan module	Carryover	Fan
Standardized parts*		Cord (mounted in cord reel) Indicator (mounted in cover) O-ring (mounted in cover) Gasket (mounted in cover)

*Solutions not suitable for integration with other modules.

were not suitable for integration with any of the nine modules. Therefore, they have been placed under the headline "standardized parts."

The modules differ slightly from the module candidates that were initially indicated in the MIM (Figure 5-3). The two module candidates, electric motor and thyristor, have been clustered to form one module. Two new modules have been added (panel module and absorbent module) since they were not suited for integration with any of the other module candidates. This is a natural result from the integration work.

_____ STEP 4: EVALUATE MODULE CONCEPT

Once a modular concept has been generated, it is most important to determine the interfaces between the modules since fixed interfaces are a condition for successful parallel activities.

For the vacuum cleaner, two kinds of interface relations have been defined: geometry (G) and energy transmitting (E). It is, of course, possible to define others, but these two are sufficient for this analysis.

In Figure 5-5, the vacuum cleaner modules have been entered into the interface matrix in expected assembly order and the interface relations have been analyzed. The following examples are marked in the figure:

1. A geometric interface connects the electric motor and the chassis, which is why a G has been entered.
2. The electric motor and the fan are joined by a geometric connection. And, energy will be transmitted from the motor to the fan, which is why both a G and an E have been entered.
3. The panel transmits electric current to the motor, which is why an E has been entered. Some kind of

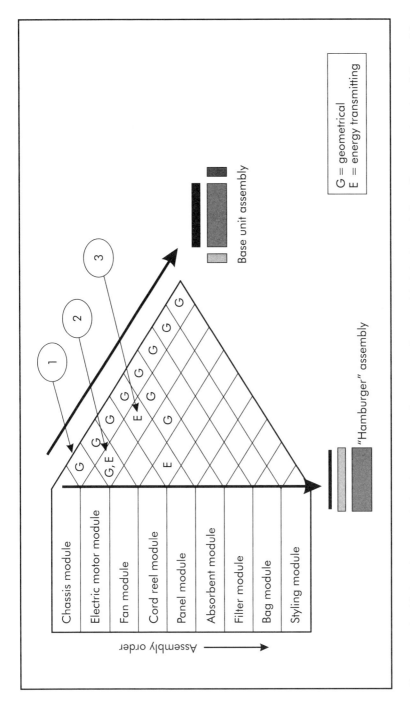

Figure 5-5. In this interface matrix for the vacuum cleaner, most geometric interfaces follow the upper border of the matrix, indicating that the vacuum cleaner can be assembled on a base unit (the chassis module).

physical contact is, of course, needed, which will give a geometric interface as well. However, this is considered to be of minor importance.

In the interface matrix for the vacuum cleaner, most geometric interfaces follow the upper border of the matrix, which means that the vacuum cleaner can be assembled on a base unit. Independently of assembly order, most modules can be mounted on the chassis.

Economic evaluation of the modular concept for the vacuum cleaner will not be presented here.

STEP 5: OPTIMIZE MODULES

At this step, module specifications are created. An example (much simplified) of such a specification is shown in Figure 5-6.

When the module specifications have been established, detailed design work for each module can begin.

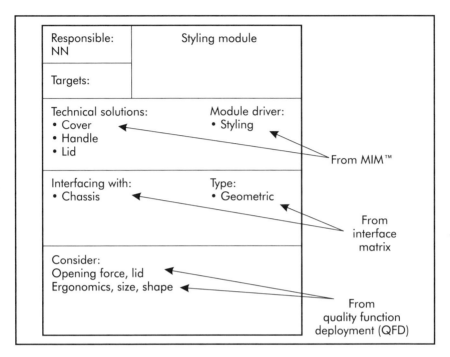

Figure 5-6. Module specification (much simplified) for the styling module. The information in the module specification is gathered from the earlier steps of the MFD™ method.

Applying MFD™ in Practice

The application field for Modular Function Deployment™ (MFD™) embodies a wide range of manufacturing companies in widely differing industries. It has been applied in modularization projects for cars, trucks, vacuum cleaners, staplers, grinding machines, train bogies, winches, servo drives, washing machines, fifth wheels, and many other products.

In this chapter, experiences from four different companies will be discussed. The purpose is to show how the MFD method can be applied and what results it may bring.

 **VOLVO CAR CORPORATION**

The Volvo case shows how the MFD method can be used in a large corporation and how it supports the managment of extensive projects. Because of confidentiality reasons, no details or quantitative results are reviewed here.

First, the new platform concept for producing cars at
Volvo is introduced. Then a short description follows of how
a complex product, such as a complete car, can be modularized. After that, modularization of the inner roof and the
front of the car is briefly described. The Module Driver™
profile is brought forward as an important tool for evaluation and comparison of different results. Finally, a new
module concept for the car door is presented. The Volvo
case study shows how the total concept of MFD helped to
revolutionize the way it produces cars.

Platform Thinking

The word *platform*, not to be confused with the bottom
plate of the car body, means that a number of predefined
models can be built from a common base. The *common base*,
according to Volvo's definition, is "everything that gives
synergy in knowledge and investments." It might be compared with a Lego® system where it is possible to build
many different cars with only a few building blocks.

Intensive efforts are required to implement a platform
strategy for the first time with considerably more exhaus-
tive analyses than for a normal new car project. The intention is, though, that it will pay off in the development of
consecutive models. Only new features, or planned design
changes, will be of concern in the coming development
projects (maybe 15 instead of the earlier 100).

Volvo's new production strategy aims at commonality
between the assembly plants in Gent (Belgium) and
Gothenburg (Sweden). The new method of vehicle design
makes it possible to build several car models from a common base concept, the "platform." Volvo introduced "platform thinking" as a new economical and customer-oriented
way of building cars. The purpose was to achieve advantages such as shortened lead times, higher efficiency in

production, and frequent model changes. This, in turn, enabled increased sales and lower costs.

With the new platform concept, it was necessary for the production systems in Gent and Gothenburg to be structured alike. With this commonality, the building of different car models could be moved quickly between the plants, corresponding to customer demands in different geographic areas.

To begin, the new production system was concurrently developed in cooperation with product development and design. Staff from the plants worked together with industrial engineers and designers to verify products and processes in the early phases of the project. Today, the assembly systems in the plants are still based on final assembly lines where the different modules are fitted to the car body. However, modularity enables pre-assembly to a larger extent than before, which shortens the final assembly lead time.

With a modularized product structure, Volvo is now able to out-source larger parts of the car to a smaller number of primary vendors (6-12). These primary vendors actively participate in product development and shorten development lead times by implementing concurrent development of modules once the interfaces have been defined.

Modularization of a Complete Car

Modularization of a complex product, such as a car, demands division into modules on several levels. Modularization on exceedingly lower levels goes on as long as it is meaningful. For manual assembly, the lower limit is about 50 assembly operations per module. Other aspects, such as the wish to create common units or variety, might make it useful to go on with modularization all the way down to single parts.

The division of a complete car into modules on the uppermost level (level 1) is, by car manufacturers, seen as more or less generic and commonplace in the industry. This originates from the evolution of so-called "functional areas," grown out of the need to manage work within a large organization. Within Volvo, this division into "natural" modules has been supported by work done on an earlier modularized concept car, the Volvo concept car (VCC). Starting out from the functional areas and with the requirement of lead time reduction, Volvo identified 18 modules on the uppermost level.

In connection with the identification of level 1 modules, Volvo conducted an analysis of the Module Drivers for the functional areas as shown in Figure 6-1. The analysis indicated functional areas with strong or very strong reasons to shape separate module areas and those with weak reasons, suited for integration.

A horizontal summation of the Module Drivers in the Module Indication Matrix™ (MIM™) showed how every single driver was weighted in the analysis (see Figure 6-2). The Module Driver profile served as a basis for interesting discussions concerning strategies, important competencies, and vital technologies.

Based on the level 1 analysis, modularization work now continued on the next module level (level 2). In the next sections, three examples of such work will be discussed: the inner roof, vehicle front, and car door. The inner roof will be described as a pure modularization case. The vehicle front discussion will focus on design team organization, and the modularization of the car door will be compared with an earlier modular door design.

The Inner Roof

In identifying the submodules of the inner roof (level 2), the project members gained valuable knowledge on how systematic modularization could be performed.

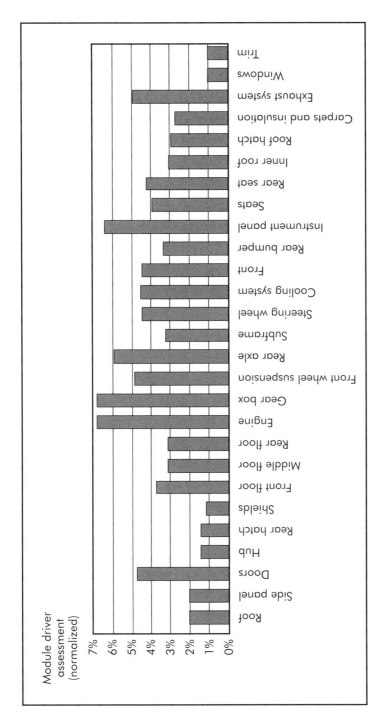

Module driver assessment (normalized)

Figure 6-1. *Module Driver™ assessment for Volvo's functional areas. Modularization of a complex product, such as a car, demands division into modules on several levels. Modularization on the uppermost level is, by car manufacturers, seen as more or less generic and commonplace in the industry. This originates from the evolution of so-called "functional areas," grown out of the need to manage work within a large organization.*

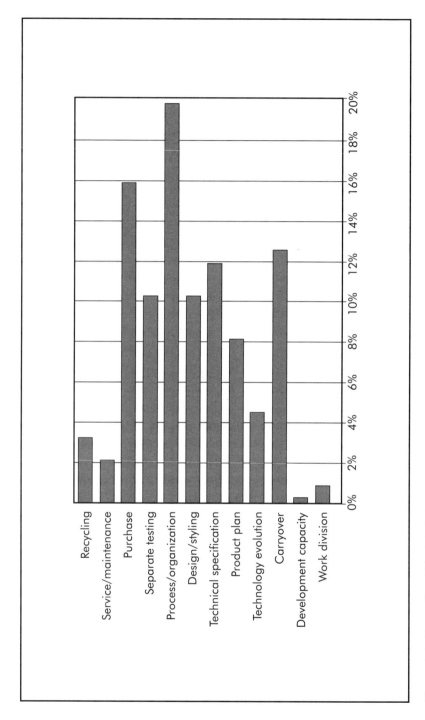

Figure 6-2. Normalized Module Driver profile for the functional areas at Volvo.

The project was driven by the production engineering department. It was agreed to work according to a simplified model of the MFD method, not incorporating a QFD analysis. Therefore, the first assignment for the team was to do a functional decomposition. That is, to address the question: "What is the function of each technical solution that is contained, or should be contained, within the inner roof?"

The ideal number of modules for the inner roof was calculated at about six, the source being that about 40 parts (or assemblies) were contained in the roof (six is the nearest square root of 40). This ideal number would be valid provided that the interfaces were so well designed that an interface assembly (modules to each other) could be accomplished in about 10 seconds per interface. If this were not possible, the ideal number would lower toward three modules (see Chapter 4). To start with, however, the team aimed at six modules. The discussions during the work were intensive, absorbing, and very rewarding. Many creative contributions and ideas came from the purchasing people as they expressed quite different and interesting views on the matter. The result of the work on the MIM is shown in Figure 6-3.

The six technical solutions having the strongest reasons to form modules were chosen, that is, the technical solutions that after the analysis had gathered the highest scores:

- sun shield;
- cables;
- reading light;
- inner light;
- braking light; and
- in-step handle.

With the MIM assessment as the basis, the rest of the technical solutions were tested for integration or grouping with one of these module candidates. Further integration between the module candidates was also attempted, but

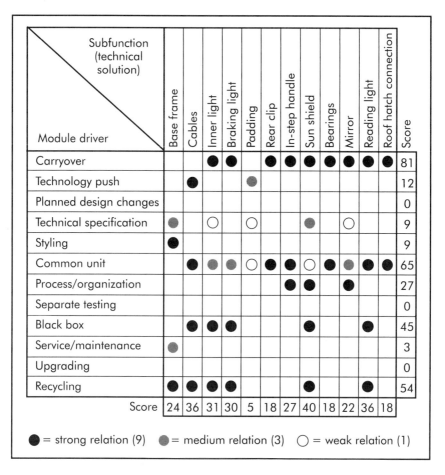

Figure 6-3. Module Indication Matrix for the inner roof.

Module driver / Subfunction (technical solution)	Base frame	Cables	Inner light	Braking light	Padding	Rear clip	In-step handle	Sun shield	Bearings	Mirror	Reading light	Roof hatch connection	Score
Carryover			●	●		●	●	●	●	●	●	●	81
Technology push	●				●								12
Planned design changes													0
Technical specification	●		○		○			●		○			9
Styling	●												9
Common unit			●	●	●	○	●	●	○	●	●	●	65
Process/organization							●	●		●			27
Separate testing													0
Black box		●	●	●				●			●		45
Service/maintenance	●												3
Upgrading													0
Recycling	●	●	●	●				●			●		54
Score	24	36	31	30	5	18	27	40	18	22	36	18	

● = strong relation (9)   ● = medium relation (3)   ○ = weak relation (1)

did not bring any further results. The final proposal is shown in Table 6-1.

Within Volvo, the responsibility for components are spread between many individuals. Roughly, each component within a car has its responsible person. This necessitated work on the inner roof project to be conducted by a large team of 15 persons, which is in conflict with the usual recommendation of 6-8 participants. As was discovered, too large a group easily becomes inefficient and difficult to

Table 6-1. Final modules composing inner roof

Module	Strongest drivers	Number of variants	Technical solutions
M1 Brake light module	Carryover Common unit	1 variant	Braking light Rear clip
M2 Sun shield module	Carryover	2 variants	Sun shield
M3 Harness module	Technical evolution	2 variants	Cable base and option
M4 Inner light module	Carryover Common unit	1 variant	Inner light
M5 Reading light module	Carryover Common unit	1 variant	Reading light
M6 Base module	Styling Recycling	2 variants (hatch or no hatch)	Base frame Bearing Padding In-step handle (Roof hatch connection)

manage. Someone often was missing, delaying the process. However, as was the case at Volvo, such difficulties tend to decrease at the same rate as the project picks up pace.

The Module Driver profile for the inner roof is shown in Figure 6-4. The weighting of the different Module Drivers (summed horizontally in the MIM) is given as a percent of the total sum given for all Module Drivers. Thus, the result is normalized and could be used for comparison with results from other teams.

It should be noted from this profile that the most weighted Module Drivers concern internal company issues (carryover, common unit, supplier available), while more customer-oriented drivers received very little attention.

65

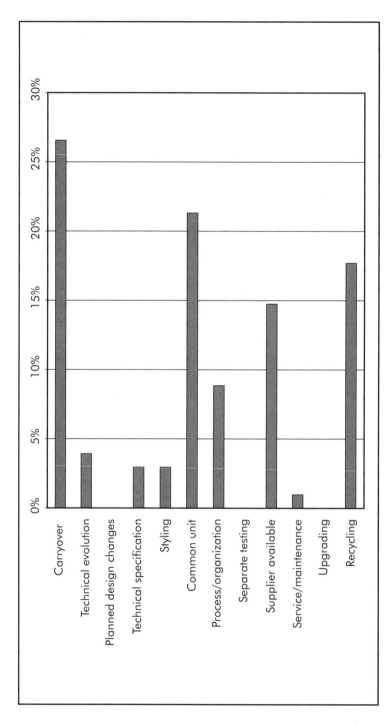

Figure 6-4. Normalized Module Driver profile for inner roof. The most weighted Module Drivers are carryover, common unit, supplier available, and recycling, which indicates that the team members are directed toward building cars as cost effectively as possible with environmental considerations in mind.

Clearly, the team values are directed toward building cars as cost effectively as possible and with respect for the environment. However, a modular product affords the opportunity to be more aggressive, using planned design changes and styling to attract customers, something that will be of even greater concern in the future.

Vehicle Front

Two separate projects concerning modularization of the car front were conducted at Volvo. One project was initiated by the production engineering department at the assembly plant for Volvo 940/60, the other by the module team for the vehicle front in the ongoing development project for new cars.

The purpose of the assembly plant project was to define how the front of existing cars could be redesigned to make assembly easier. Before modularization, the front assembly created assembly line balance problems, and the assembly work contained many ergonomically uncomfortable conditions. The operator often had to crawl down into the engine compartment to be able to fit all the components. A front module that, under better working conditions, could be pre-assembled and then fitted complete onto the chassis, was desired.

The purpose of the new car project was to evaluate the MFD method and give the vehicle front team the necessary data for a future modularized front (level 2).

In the project initiated by the assembly plant, the work was conducted in a team mostly made up from production engineering staff, while the new car project was conducted in a cross functional team, dominated by process planning staff.

Confidentiality reasons prohibit the account of the modularization itself and the resulting design proposal for the vehicle front. Instead, the different focus (assessment of Module Drivers) of the two teams will be discussed.

Figure 6-5 shows details of the different Module Driver profiles generated by each team. For further comparison, the profile for the inner roof is also included. A comparison between the production engineering team and the vehicle front team (the new car project), reveals that the production engineering team focused on a modular design to simplify assembly work. The search for common units and carryover can clearly be seen. A modular design with a high percentage of such features will improve the possibilities for increased automation and lengthen amortization periods for equipment. That is, it will create conditions that make manual assembly work easier.

At the same time, it is clear that the production engineering team does not expect a higher degree of technical evolution and/or planned development. The vehicle front team, having a higher degree of cross functionality, has slightly greater expectations. A far-sighted modularization provides for needs within both process and product development. However, this requires that all interests are represented on the project team, in other words, a cross-functional project team.

Comparison with the inner roof Module Driver profile shows that different parts in a product have different property demands. The inner roof profile reveals stronger reasons to form a module for easier recycling than the vehicle front, so those functions involved with the inner roof should have special competence in material and environmental issues. The driver profile serves as an excellent base for choice and allocation of resources and competencies within different parts of the company. It also serves well when coordinating work in different module areas to achieve overall company strategic objectives.

In Figure 6-5, it can be see that all teams have focused on the purchase driver, which might reflect the overall trend in the car industry today. A high degree of integration is sought, with a limited number of vendors who are responsible for complete systems.

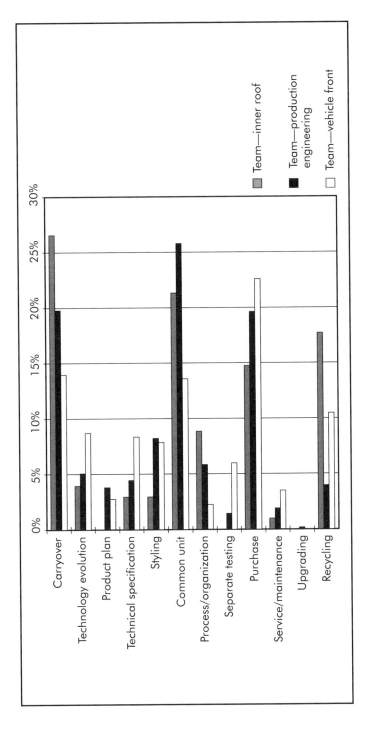

Figure 6-5. Module Driver profile for three different modularization projects at Volvo. The production engineering team focused on the Module Drivers common unit and carryover, which indicates their search for a modular design to simplify assembly work. The vehicle front team, having a higher degree of cross functionality, had slightly greater expectations for the development of the front. Comparison with the inner roof shows that different parts in a product have different property demands. For instance, the inner roof has stronger reasons for recycling than the front.

Car Door

In earlier research, modularization of a car door (inside) was studied in connection with the introduction of Volvo's model 800. In the 800 model, assembled directly on the final line, all parts in the glass lifting device were grouped into a so-called "door cassette" that could be outsourced to a vendor. In doing so, it was assumed the assembly costs would be reduced by 60%. The door cassette, however, actually increased logistics costs because a special packing material was required. This had not been assessed during the modularization of the door. Also, the door cassette only fit the 800 car model.

Two engineering students from the Chalmers Institute of Technology (Gothenburg), in cooperation with Volvo staff, conducted a new systematic modularization supported by the MFD™ method for the door in the new car project. The objective was to improve the cassette design by creating a more holistic base for the modularization. This time, the work encompassed all the subsystems in the door, not just the glass lifting device.

The resulting proposal indicated that the door should be divided into seven modules (corresponds to the "rule of thumb" square root of the total number of assembly operations). It is interesting that the new design did not contain a complete lift cassette. Instead, a divided lifting device was proposed. Because of its common unit driver, the driving motor was proposed to be integrated in a larger "inside plate" module. The lift rail was grouped together with the glass in a type-dependent variant module. Space requirement led to two different solutions for the lift rail, one with a wire lift and the other with a cross-arm lift. If the lifting mechanism was integrated with the inside plate, it would disturb the commonality and prove unsatisfactory.

The car door example shows the necessity to implement a holistic approach to modularization before a particular module concept is adopted. Otherwise, there is an obvious risk for suboptimized modules.

ATLAS COPCO CONTROLS

Atlas Copco Controls (ACC) develops and manufactures customized electronic products. Producing mainly servo drives, it has 300 different types, half of which are standard and half of which are customized. Of the 300 variants, about 60 represent 80% of the total yearly volume of 100,000 units.

Important changes in product design and company organization in the beginning of the 1990s put ACC on the road to modularization and component standardization. The standard assortment has been functionally and electronically modularized and can be customized by reprogramming the software.

Customer-specific drives, on the other hand, required prototypes to be built. Lead time for a prototype was 3–4 months in early 1996. It then took 1–2 years for the new prototype to be field tested and adjusted. The designer had access to a component database and often reused earlier solutions for some parts of the prototype. However, there was no defined platform to build prototypes from and new parts were often added when a customer-specific product was developed.

The prevailing understanding among companies in the customized electronics business is that the lowest production costs are achieved through maximal integration of components on one single board. This has been seen as a strong opponent to modularization. However, the customer variation aspect and fitting of the product design to production processes more strongly favor modularization. In developing a new product generation, ACC decided to go for a modular design using the MFD method since it forces the design team to consider the entire life cycle of the product.

The drive contains parts for logical control, input and output functions, and a power supply. The power for the electronics inside is assembled close to the sensitive logical components. The combination of different components can give an infinite number of variants. Some special components have long delivery times and are costly.

Upon review, the original technical solutions contained in the product were considered satisfactory and directly transferred to the MIM. With a large quantity of electronic circuit components assembled on boards, the "rule of thumb" for the ideal number of modules could be misleading. In a case like this, it was appropriate to disregard the automatically surface-mounted components for the calculation. The remaining components, about 60, corresponded to about eight modules as the ideal preference (eight is the nearest square root of 60).

Six of the highest weighted technical solutions in the MIM™ were selected together with the power factor controller (PFC), since the PFC is an optional function requested only by a few customers. Thus, seven module candidates were selected:

- power stage;
- CPU (central processing unit);
- rectifier equipment (with capacitor);
- logic voltage (input/output [I/O]);
- gate driver;
- current sensor; and the
- PFC (power factor controller).

With these candidates as starting point, different module concepts were generated and evaluated. The four main modules of the finally chosen concept are presented in Figure 6-6. The term 1/2 rectifier originates from the split of this component into a high-voltage part and a logic part due to conflicting Module Drivers within the rectifier. The modules are outlined as follows:

1. The CPU module, which includes I/O (logic parts) and communication. The Module Drivers were carryover, process/organization, separate testing, and service/maintenance.

2. A power stage module, which includes the gate driver, and short circuit and temperature sensors. The Module Drivers were carryover, common unit, process/organization, separate testing, and service/maintenance.

3. The main board module, which includes PFC, current sensor, logic voltage, 1/2 rectifier (logic part), I/O (voltage and current transformation), and communication. The Module Drivers were different specification and process/organization.

4. The 1/2 rectifier module (high voltage), whose Module Drivers were carryover, common unit, process/organization, separate testing, and service/maintenance.

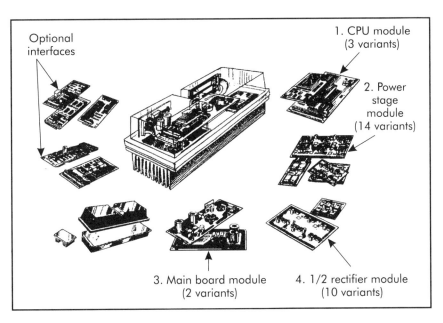

Figure 6-6. Atlas Copco Control's modularized servo drives.

73

The horizontal summation and normalization of the weights per Module Driver gives the driver profile of the product shown in Figure 6-7. If the driver profile shows inconsistency with company strategy, another iteration of the work might be appropriate.

The ACC driver profile shows high percentages for the carryover and technology evolution drivers. This reveals a strong intention to carry over modules to new product generations, and, at the same time, it highlights the necessity to be prepared for technology evolution outside of the company's control. The common unit and different specification items are also fairly highly weighted, reflecting the company's intentions to reuse modules over the entire assortment of products while still fulfilling the customers' differing requirements. Process/organization, separate test-

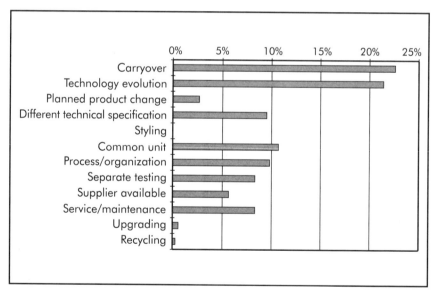

Figure 6-7. The Module Driver profile for ACC's servo drives shows high percentages for the carryover and technology evolution drivers, which reveals ACC's intention to carry over modules to new product generations and at the same time prepare for technology evolution outside the company's control.

ing, and service/maintenance are held important because of efforts within ACC to adapt product design to the production process and maintain quality and service.

Modularization demands simple, fixed, and well-specified interfaces. For instance, the modules "power stage" and "1/2 rectifier" both require secured heat transfer to the chassis. They also need to be electrically connected to the main board and CPU. An innovation gave an easy-to-assemble solution that connects the boards (electrically) and secures the contact with the chassis. The module's main board and CPU have to be connected as well. Service and upgrading aspects revealed the need for a socket connector. However, no reliable socket was found, so the CPU was hole mounted on the main board.

The resulting modular product design yielded the following general effects:

- A reduction of lead time in product development from the earlier 3–4 months to prototype and 1–2 years to secured product, to 2 months to prototype and 6 months to secured product in full scale production.
- Only new modules need testing and certification if the rest of the included modules are already certified, allowing easier compliance to standards.
- New processes are easier to introduce. Quality is improved when single modules are tested before final assembly. The results were: 10% increased logistic efficiency; 5% increased commonality; 5% shorter lead times; and 300% higher inventory turnover.
- Final assembly time was reduced from 30 to 10 minutes.

The greatest improvements were reduced product cost, reduced lead time in assembly, and the ease of variant creation. However, improvements to the interfaces are still needed to increase the ability for rapid development of new products.

VBG

VBG Ltd., Manchester, United Kingdom is a subsidiary of VBG Sweden. VBG Ltd. has a market-leading position in England, with almost 50% of its sales volume from fifth wheels. This case study will treat two different aspects of modularization. First, a case from VBG Ltd. in England will show how the MFD and design for assembly (DFA) methods (Boothroyd and Dewhurst 1994) complement one another. DFA strives for the integration of parts to arrive at a product design that is as easy to assemble as possible, while MFD reveals when integration should be avoided because of other strategic reasons (the Module Drivers). Second, how the production system is configured based on a modular product concept is shown through the example of the modularization of drawbar couplings at VBG in Sweden.

Fifth Wheel

A fifth wheel is a coupling device between a tractor (pulling truck without integrated truck bed) and semi-trailer as shown in Figure 6-8. The fifth wheel is mounted on the tractor chassis and connects to a kingpin on the semi-trailer.

At VBG, the modularization work for the fifth wheel was conducted in six major steps:

1. Function analysis of existing design;
2. DFA analysis of existing design;
3. Module Driver analysis of existing design;
4. Redesign supported by the conducted analyses;
5. DFA analysis of each module; and
6. Evaluation of generated module concept.

Figure 6-9 describes the functional decomposition of the product with the help of a functions-and-means tree. From the figure, the main function is "connect tractor to

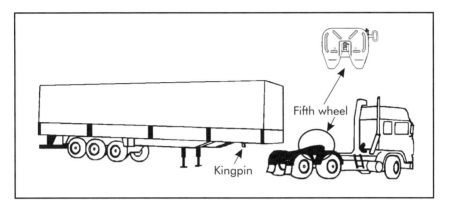

Figure 6-8. The VBG fifth wheel is mounted on the tractor chassis and connects to a kingpin on the semi-trailer.

trailer" and the corresponding technical solution is "kingpin and mechanical coupling."

The succeeding DFA analysis showed that the number of parts contained in the fifth wheel could be dramatically reduced. It also indicated a number of areas with potential for design improvements. However, the team was invited to wait on the generation of redesign suggestions until the Module Driver analysis had been completed. The original design is shown in Figure 6-10.

Figure 6-11 shows the MIM for the fifth wheel. As explained earlier, every technical solution is assessed against each of the Module Drivers. The module candidates can then be picked out, and the grouping or integration of other technical solutions with the module candidates is executed, depending upon the module driver match.

With the DFA and MFD analyses as a basis, the product was redesigned. The resulting modular product design is shown in Figure 6-12.

To compare the old and new design, another DFA analysis, this time for each module, was conducted. The analysis revealed that the number of parts contained in the product

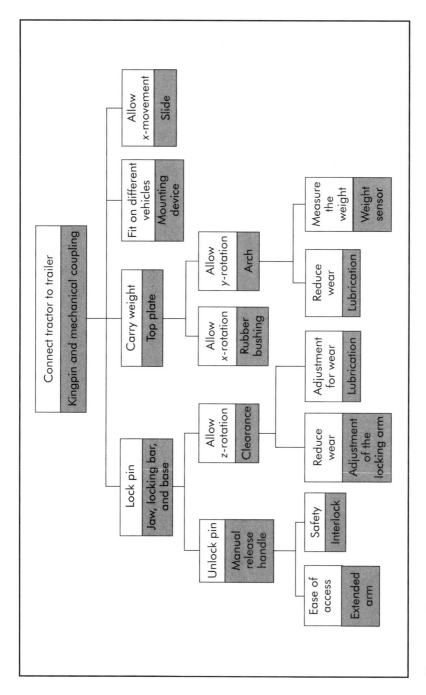

Figure 6-9. Functions-and-means tree for the VBG fifth wheel.

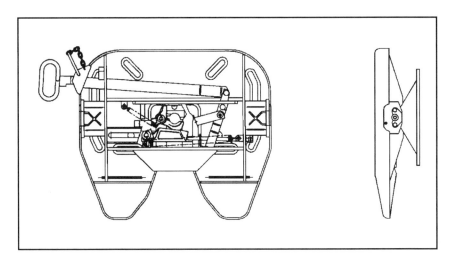

Figure 6-10. The VBG fifth wheel, old design.

had been reduced by 42% and the assembly time reduction was about 56%.

An economical evaluation of the module concept was carried out. Here it is interesting to point out that a traditional calculation, considering costs for material, labor, investment, etc., showed no profit for the module concept. However, supplementary consideration was given to benefits such as the effect on quality assurance, data processing, purchasing, inventory control, stock levels, and workshop space. The result of the extended calculation made company management decide to proceed with modularization.

Drawbar Coupling

VBG Products AB in Vänersborg, Sweden manufactures and sells complete systems for the connection of trucks and trailers. The company leads the market in Scandinavia and its customers are mainly retailers that supply end customers with fully equipped trucks.

Legend:
- ● = strong relation (9)
- ◐ = medium relation (3)
- ○ = weak relation (1)

Technical solution	Carryover	Technical evolution	Planned product changes	Different specification	Styling	Common unit	Process/organization	Separate testing	Supplier available	Service/maintenance	Upgrading	Recycling	Score	Candidates
Arch assembly (LH,RH)	●					●			○				19	
Arch (2x)				●	●	●			●	●			36	X
Base weld assembly				●	○	●				◐			22	X
Front crossmember	●					●			○				19	
Rear crossmember	●					●			○				19	
Jaw				●	○	●			●	●			37	X
Lock bar				●		●			●	●			36	X
Jaw pin	●					●			●	●			36	X
Lock bar pin	●					●			●	●			36	X
Pushlink lever assembly				●		●			◐	○			22	
Handle				●	●				○	●			28	X
Cover plate weld assembly				●		●							18	
Saddle plate weld assembly	●					●							18	
Safety clip bracket	●					●							18	
Adjustment stud	●					●			○	○			20	
Tail gusset	●					●			○				19	
Top plate	●					●							18	
Bolt (handle)	●					●							18	

Module driver groups: Development and design (Carryover, Technical evolution, Planned product changes); Variance (Different specification, Styling); Manufacturing (Common unit, Process/organization); Quality (Separate testing); Purchase (Supplier available); After-sales (Service/maintenance, Upgrading, Recycling).

Figure 6-11. Module Indication Matrix for the VBG fifth wheel. The technical solutions "arch," "base weld assembly," "jaw," "lock bar," "jaw pin," "lock bar pin," and "handle" have been picked out as module candidates.

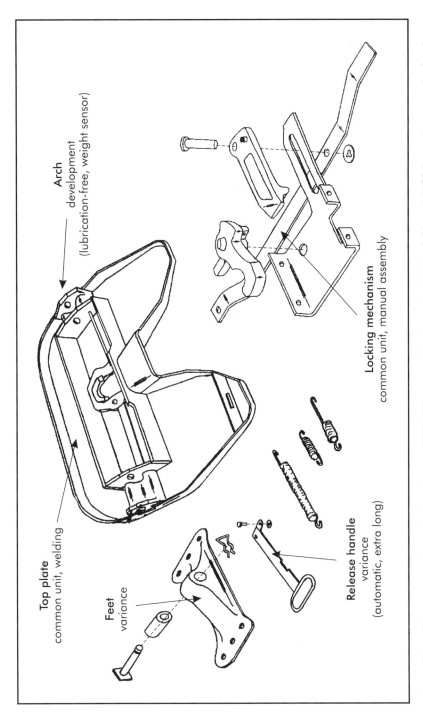

Figure 6-12. The new, modular design for the VBG fifth wheel developed with the DFA and MFD™ analyses as the basis.

For VBG, the order flow varied strongly. Production was customer controlled, that is, variations in the number of incoming orders were managed by permitting overtime, re-allocating resources, and hiring temporary personnel. Order peaks existed before summer and Christmas. These peaks were so prominent that inventory would need to be built up long before it was needed.

In the original design, the coupler had the same life cycle as the truck, except for some wearing parts that were replaced every second year. Retailers and branch offices kept their own spare parts inventory, but the logistics and manufacture of spare parts still caused VBG difficulties.

Before the modularization project was started, the assortment contained a large number of variants, mostly consisting of unique parts. The company suffered from high purchase costs and long lead and setup times in manufacturing and assembly. It was also clear that the products would be influenced by the new European standards, which would increase the demand for control and documentation.

The objective of the modularization project was to maintain a large product range with fewer unique parts per variant. One prerequisite was that the new modules would also have to fit as spare parts for older couplings.

The MFD method was used to design a new drawbar coupling assortment with a product range as large as earlier. The new modularized coupler is shown in Figure 6-13. The coupler is comprised of three main modules: catch mouth, mechanism, and connecting package. Two optional modules were also defined: air servo and wire servo.

Because of the new modular design, the number of raw parts (forging and casting) was dramatically reduced. The purchase costs were also reduced since the delivery quantity per variant increased. Table 6-2 shows a comparison of the old and new concept part requirements.

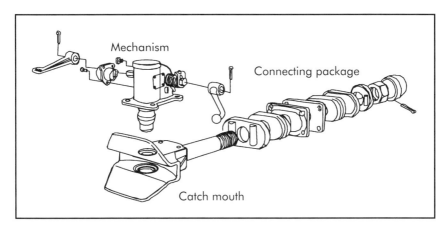

Figure 6-13. The modularized VBG drawbar coupling. The new coupler is comprised of three main modules: catch mouth, mechanism, and connecting package.

Table 6-2. Comparison of old and new concept part requirements

Component	Old concept	New concept
Mechanism (raw part)	10	3
Bolt	13	6
Raw hoop	11	5
Catch mouth	1	3
Bushing	18	7
Connector	7	7
Total	60	31

The general benefits from the implementation of the new modular design concept are described by VBG to be:

- reduced lead times for product development through concurrent development activities, use of carryover designs, and simplified certification;
- reduced lead times in production (from 21 days to 3 days);

83

- lower production costs because of less need for tooling, reduced setup time, fewer handling activities, and increased possibility for automation;
- less working capital because of fewer different parts in stock, decreased spare parts stock levels, and later variant creation in production; and
- reduced purchase costs because of fewer different components and increased purchase volume per component.

A New Production System Based on a Modular Product

VBG decided to reorganize the production system to accommodate the new modular concept. The objective was to create a factory adapted for controlled development.

To begin, a vision of the future production system was created. A foreseeable future for VBG was about 5 years. A fully optimized production system was planned to be in operation in 1999. The vision was then translated backwards, step by step, until the production system for the current needs was reached (1995). The methodology may seem simple, but a lot of work is needed to get the right information and to foresee future needs.

The factory layout follows the principle "products within the product—small factories within the factory," so the modular product structure is reflected in the production system. Based on the module specifications for the drawbar coupling, a plan for each module area was established. An example of such a plan is shown in Figure 6-14. Some information has been excluded because of confidentiality reasons.

Based on the module area plans, the fully optimized factory layout for 1999 was set up as shown in Figure 6-15. The layout consists of three module areas containing both manufacture and assembly: top plate and lock mechanism, arch cell, and component production.

Module Area Plan

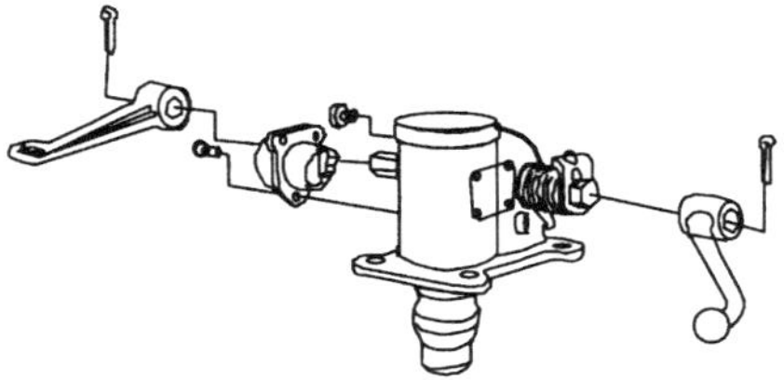

Product: Drawbar coupling

Module: Mechanism

Rev./ Date:

Cost targets:

XXXXX

YYYYY

Year	1995	1996	1997	1998	1999
Module data					
Volume	30,000	32,000	40,000	45,000	50,000
Number of variants	10	4	7	7	7
Number of part numbers	35	35	22	22	22
Number pf parts	45	45	31	31	31
Process changes					
Surface treatment		XXX			
Component manufacture	XXX				
Assembly					
Production targets					
Lead time	21 days	7 days	7 days	4 days	4 days

Figure 6-14. Module area plan for the mechanism module.

Component manufacture

	7–14 days	7 days	7 days	2 days	1–2 days
Lead time	7–14 days	7 days	7 days	2 days	1–2 days
Needed capacity	3,900 hr/year	3,900 hr/year	5,200 hr/year	5,850 hr/year	6,500 hr/year
Needed labor	3 persons	3 persons	3.6 persons	3.9 persons	4.3 persons
Production stock level	3 weeks	3 weeks	3 weeks	0	0
Peak stock level production	maximum 1 week	maximum 1 week	maximum 1 week	maximum 1 week	maximum 1 week
Peak stock level market	4 weeks	4 weeks	4 weeks	4 weeks	4 weeks
Setup time	132 minutes	0 (54) minutes	0 (54) minutes	0	0
Batch size					

Assembly

	7 days	7 days	7 days	1 day	1 day
Lead time	7 days	7 days	7 days	1 day	1 day
Capacity demand	3,000 hr/year	3,000 hr/year	4,000 hr/year	4,500 hr/year	5,000 hr/year
Labor demand	2.7 persons	2.7 persons	2.7 persons	3.0 persons	3.3 persons
Peak stock level	0	0	0	0	x (0)
Setup time	48 minutes	48 minutes	10 minutes		
Needed labor*	3.0 persons	3.6 persons	4.0 persons	4.5 persons	5.0 persons

* Built on the approximation that real labor demand is 1.5 × assembly time

Batch size $= B \times S/(buT - Bt)$
where:
B = need per day
S = setup time
b = allowance factor
u = equipment availability (%)
T = available time per day
t = manufacture or assembly time

Lead time = WIP/output per hour
where:
WIP = work-in-progress

Figure 6-14. (continued)

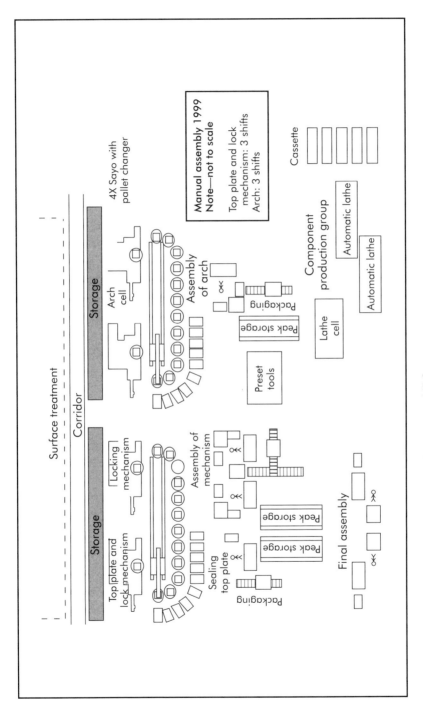

Figure 6-15. Fully optimized factory layout for 1999 at VBG.

Following the stepwise development described in the module area plans, a factory layout for 1996 was then derived (Figure 6-16), which specified the development steps conducting to the layout of 1999. Thus, VBG created a factory adapted for continuous and controlled development, with the ability to accommodate increasing capacity demands.

The goals established for lead time reduction and rationalization implied extended responsibilities for the production staff. VBG chose to create goal-oriented groups for the module and component manufacturing areas. Their main tasks were:

- production planning;
- planning of peak stock levels;
- material requirements planning; and
- preventive service and maintenance on machines.

In the 1999 factory layout, much of the order administration is to be handled by the production groups.

The information handling system will be an important part of the 1999 factory layout. Its guiding star will be simplicity—short information links where most of the administration is handled directly by the production groups.

SEPSON

Sepson is a small Swedish company that produces mobile winches (Figure 6-17). Most winches are hydraulically driven and made for adaptation on vehicles such as tractors, rescue cars, and trucks. It was determined that the number of variants in the product assortment had grown out of control and the product design had to be renewed.

The modularization project generated a new concept for winches, consisting of six modules. Three of the modules were variant modules and the rest were common units.

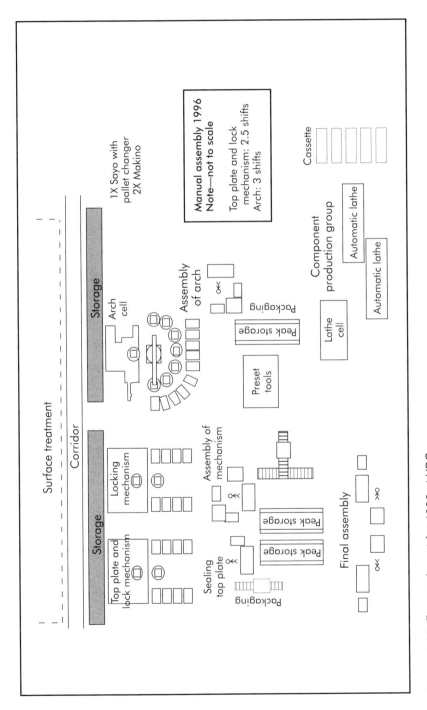

Figure 6-16. Factory layout for 1996 at VBG.

With the new modular design, a typical winch uses seven modules (including two gear-box modules). Through various combinations of the six modules, 28 variants of winches can be created. Table 6-3 compares the former conventional design with the new modular design.

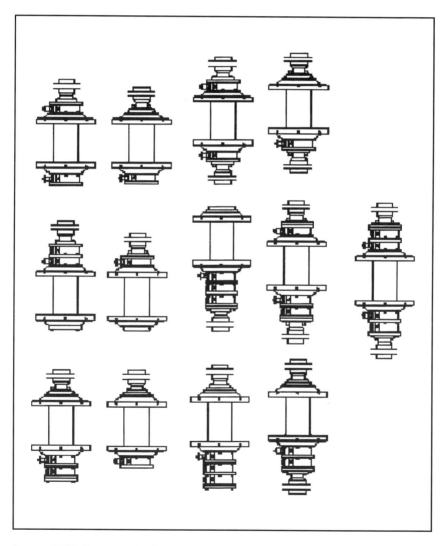

Figure 6-17. Sepson winches.

**Table 6-3. Comparison of conventional design
with new modular design for winches**

	Conventional design	Modular design
Number of modules per product	—	7
Number of modules in assortment	—	10
Number of parts in product	119	84
Number of different parts in product	51	28
Number of different parts in assortment	107	32
Assembly time per product, seconds	1,200	751
Number of drawings in A4 equivalents	91	45

In an evolutionary project, the modular product concept proved to be beneficial in many respects related to the product development effort (Erixon et al. 1996). What at firsthand appeared to be a complex project, became easy to manage. The modular concept also enabled flexibility in other matters:

- Fixed interfaces and the good product structure overview reduced information and managerial needs and allowed design work for some modules to be easily transferred to external consultants.
- Cost reduction programs for one or a few modules could start immediately.

In addition, multiple use of parts increased since the designers could quickly identify earlier used parts in the different modules. And, the generation of documentation could be easily automated, with an estimated lead time reduction (for generation of a customized manual) of from 2 weeks to 15 minutes.

Modular Product Platform Management

Modular product platform management is about reducing internal complexity, increasing flexibility, and creating a proactive organization. With a modular product structure, balance can be achieved between measures aimed at cost-cutting and those aimed at enlarging market shares.

THE LINK BETWEEN STRATEGY AND DEVELOPMENT

For a company to be successful, its strategy must be explicitly stated, understood by all, and reflected in the heart of the company—the product. The company strategy includes long-term goals and tactics concerning how the company should act to achieve its goals. These overlapping plans then need to be translated to the more concrete operational levels. Product platform strategies should be derived from the company strategy.

Before a modularization project is begun, areas such as company objectives, core competence, and potential markets need to be well defined since they strongly influence the modular structure. In this definition process, many issues will surface that will require extra attention. From here, a development plan should be set up for the product platform, containing product features to be launched, cost reductions to be managed, new technology to be introduced, and so forth. From the platform plan, a project portfolio can be derived with a rough estimate of time and resources.

On the next level, action plans for the modules can be created (see Figure 7-1). Then, necessary resources and competencies can be allocated per module.

The first step of the MFD™ method will provide a clear picture of customer preferences. Some of the target values for the product properties might not be fulfilled in time for the first product generation. Instead of postponing the launching date, the stepwise development for the technical solutions bearing this property should be outlined.

It is strategically important to uncover the company's development potential. Frequent product launches are, in many markets, the most powerful weapon in competition. Of course, areas considered as core competence should be subject for continuous improvement. "One step ahead of the competitors" must be every successful company's motto.

It is the product and the product-related services that will ultimately determine the customers' satisfaction with the product. It is therefore of great importance to make sure that the product properties correspond to the customers' expectations.

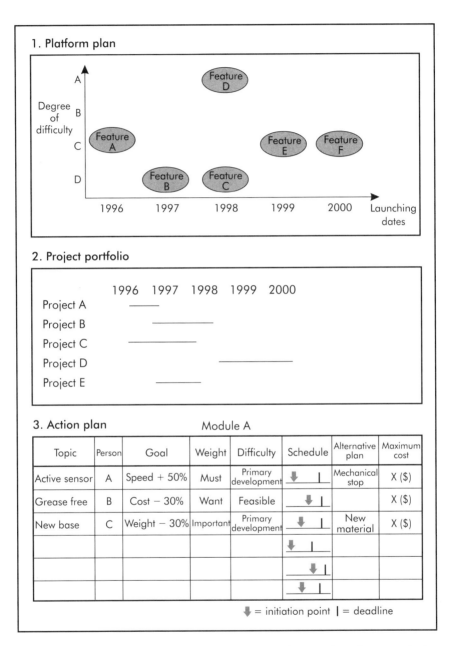

Figure 7-1. A platform development plan contains product features to be launched, cost reductions to be managed, new technology to be introduced, etc. From the platform plan, a project portfolio can be derived and on the next level action plans for the modules can be set up.

All development plans need to be revised continuously. The sales and marketing function of the company will provide important information about eventual changes in customer demands. And, technology evolution must be closely watched.

It may seem obvious that the company strategy should guide the entire organization. However, many companies suffer because their strategies are vaguely expressed and rest only on a theoretical level. Modularization will provide the means for the company to link its strategy to product development.

TAKE AND KEEP THE LEAD

To take and keep a market-leading position, a company must be able to introduce new features or other product improvements to the market in an increasingly intensive flow. However, the speed of the development process cannot just be intensified. The demand for frequent product launches has made it impossible to develop a brand new product each time.

A modularized product permits focusing on limited parts of the product at a time. The development resources can be assigned to specific, strategically important areas, and all other technical solutions can be carried over from previous product generations. If the MFD method has been worked through, the areas relevant to development efforts will surface in a number of modules with development as the main module driver. A modular product structure will assure that design changes do not widely spread within the product. Instead, they will rest only within the development modules.

A good modular structure will have modules that are used not only in one product, but in the entire assortment or large parts of it. Therefore, the development efforts will not be of use to only a single product, but to all products containing the specific module.

It is of great importance to minimize the uncertainty of the development projects within a product platform and make sure that they can be managed with good time accuracy. Therefore, "primary development" should be distinguished from "product development."

Primary development is understood to be technical evolution of new functions or products. Characteristic of primary development is that the technical solutions are unknown to the company and, therefore, these projects are hard to plan and specify.

The results from the primary development projects should be used in the product development projects. Product development is understood to be development of already known technical solutions.

By distinguishing between primary development and product development, economical and technical risks can be reduced. The organization will also find more time to handle the development's impact on production, quality issues, administration, or any other area affected by the changes.

CONTROL AND MANAGE VARIETY

A competitive environment forces companies to concentrate on many smaller market segments. Each market segment is characterized by its own demands and wishes, which means that for the company, the number of product variants dramatically increases. This can become a serious problem if the company loses control. A small, customer-driven design modification may spread widely within the product, and when all adaptation activities have been executed, it can be hard to assure that profit margins are generous enough.

Modularization does not mean standardization in the sense of reducing the customer's choice—that would be devastating. Instead, modularization means managing and controlling variance by establishing an intelligently shaped product structure.

During the modularization process, areas in the product where it is strategically important to offer the customers variance are identified. Well thought out interfaces will assure that the variations are concentrated to only these parts of the product and will not influence any other parts.

An example of a modularized product structure is schematically represented in Figure 7-2.

To make the most of a modularized product structure, it is important that the sales organization understand what advantages the module concept brings, such as low costs for products within the platform, proven design, quality, flexibility, product upgrade possibilities, short delivery lead times, and fast and correct quotations. However, the salespeople also must be aware of limitations, such as possible combinations of modules and the predefined variants of each module. A lack of understanding might result in new variants, which do not fit in the platform, negating cost reduction efforts.

A well-defined product structure serves as an excellent base for sales support since the modules can be specified and priced. This gives the sales force a unique possibility to sit down with the customer, configure the product, and immediately get an idea of price. With sales support software, a complete quotation can be obtained.

If the module concept has been thoroughly generated, the absolute majority of the customers' demands and expectations should be satisfied. If a customer should demand a product variant outside the predefined structure, it becomes a strategic question as to whether to accept the order or not. In any case, a modularized product structure provides favorable conditions for estimating the costs

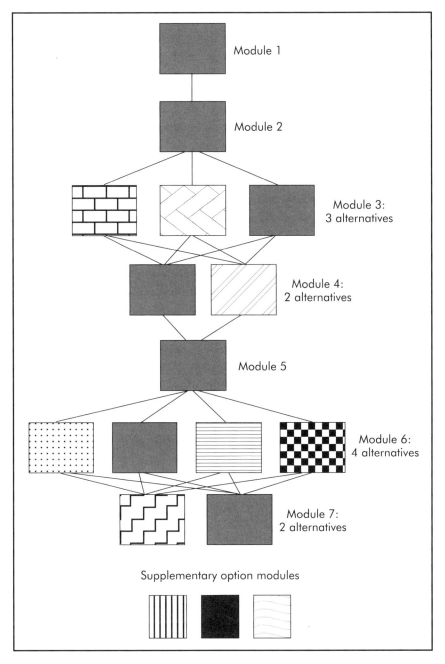

Figure 7-2. Schematic representation of a modular product structure. In this example, there are 48 possible product variants plus three additional options.

incurred for the design modifications. Thereafter, company management must decide what policy to adopt.

—————————— STRUCTURED WORKING METHODS

Product development is often considered to be complicated. There is a need to evaluate and choose between different solutions and actions. To speed up and control the process, a systematic approach is needed. The product development process should be characterized by *how* things are done, not by *who* does them.

Many companies believe they have a rather well-defined process beginning at the point where detailed product design begins. However, the hardest part, and maybe the most important, starts well before that—the concept phase.

The concept phase of the design process can be seen as a chain of iterations in which solutions are discarded, reworked, or newly invented. This may be illustrated by a funnel where the input is an infinite number of possibilities and product ideas, and where a product platform and a product platform development plan is the resulting output (see Figure 7-3).

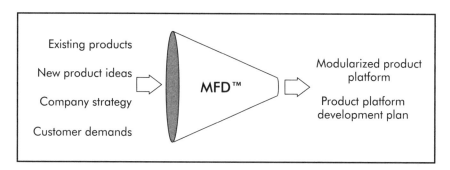

Figure 7-3. The MFD™ funnel. The input is an infinite number of possibilities and product ideas; the output is a modularized product platform together with a product platform development plan.

During the concept phase, much of the future costs for the product are determined. The product structure is fixed. How the product can be changed to fit varying requirements occurring during its lifetime is established. Therefore, in this phase, it is most important to consider the entire life cycle of the product, from development to recycling.

To assure that all aspects are considered in the concept phase, representatives from the different company functions should be present. Cross-functionality is absolutely necessary. However, it is not always that easy. Persons coming from different areas of the company may have very different views of the product and the product strategy to be applied.

The difficulties encountered with a cross-functional team are greatly diminished by using tools such as quality function deployment (QFD) and the Module Indication Matrix™ (MIM™). The use of these systematic working methods prevents irrational and personal preferences from dominating the discussions. Instead, objective evaluations can be used to guide the decision makers.

The MFD method is used throughout the concept phase of the product development process, from product idea to computer-aided design (CAD) drawing. By using a systematic approach where the work is continuously documented, the traceability is assured. All facts and judgements forming the basis of earlier made decisions are accessible. This increases the organization's ability to "make it right the first time."

Successful implementation of product modularity and the MFD method requires company management's full support and understanding. Since the MFD method puts an emphasis on the early phases of product development, it is necessary that a product development project be assigned enough time and resources in the very beginning. A person not familiar with the method might find that a lot of time is spent before there are actual results (CAD drawings).

A team working with the MFD method for the first time generally needs some external support to keep considerations and discussions on a reasonable level of detail. Once the process has been worked through, the team members will have gained experience, which will help them in future projects.

It is important that all designers learn enough about product modularity to understand the impact of design changes that affect the interfaces, and thereby the modular product structure. They also should be encouraged to optimize their designs, not only considering their influence on direct material and labor, but on all activities within the company.

BUILDING "SMALL FACTORIES WITHIN THE FACTORY"

In the same way as modules form products within the product, small factories within the factory can be built (see Figure 7-4). Production lead time is dramatically reduced by splitting long lines into parallel production of modules. And, short feedback links are assured when the modules are tested before final assembly.

Each module area should be designed to match the characteristics of the module:

- A carryover module suggests a long lifetime for the production area, so heavier investments in capital equipment can be afforded.
- A common unit module means increased production volumes are planned. The possibilities for automation are good.
- A variance module implies that the module area must be able to manage many part numbers. Material handling resources and an effective ordering system is needed.

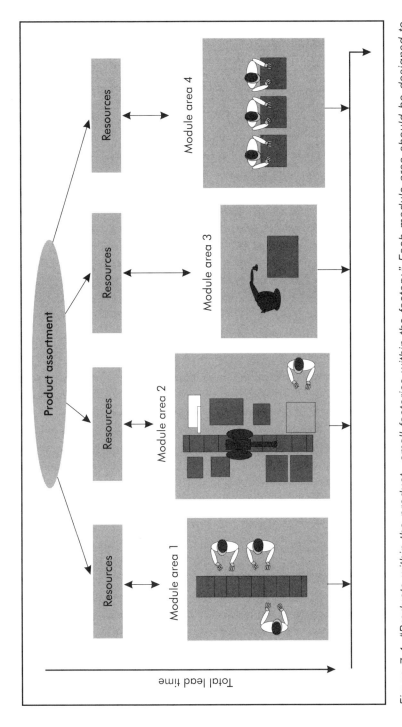

Figure 7-4. "Products within the product—small factories within the factory." Each module area should be designed to match the characteristics of the module. A carryover module, for instance, implicates a long lifetime for the production area, which means that heavier investments in capital equipment can be afforded.

- A module affected by development means that frequent changes of the module area might be necessary. This area should be characterized by flexibility.

Integrated development of the product and production system, also called concurrent engineering, is favored by this approach. A module area can be developed without interfering with any other areas. If a module is changed, this will only affect the corresponding module area, provided that the interfaces remain fixed (see Figure 7-5).

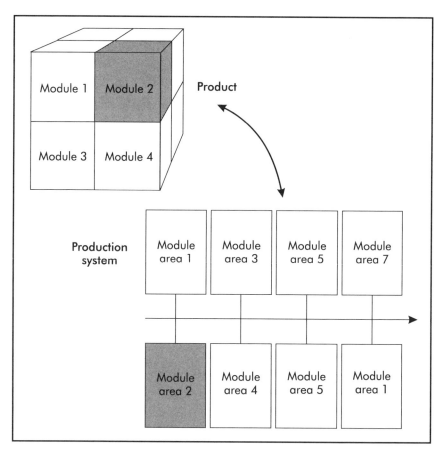

Figure 7-5. The relationship between product and production system is shown. If a module is changed, this will only affect the corresponding module area, provided the interfaces remain fixed.

A corresponding development plan for each module's production area can be derived from the module development plan. These plans will support predictable stepwise development of the production system. This also results in more successful investments since the economical risks are minimized through balanced, partial investments. And, technical risks are minimized by implementing smaller subsystems at a time. Large projects can be divided into smaller ones that have a greater possibility of meeting budgeted costs and targeted deadlines.

Appendix A: Evaluation of Module Concepts

An overview of the resulting effects and corresponding product characteristics/dependence for module concepts is given in Table A-1. Each evaluation parameter will be expanded upon in the following sections.

Table A-1. Overview of module concepts

Effect	Product characteristics/ dependence	Metric/ rule
Lead time in development	Interface complexity	Metric
Development costs	Share of carryover	Rule
Development capacity	Share of purchased modules	Rule
Product costs	Assortment complexity	Metric
System costs	Share of purchased modules	Rule
Overall lead time	Number of modules in product	Metric
Quality	Share of separately tested modules	Metric
Variant flexibility	Multiple use	Metric
Service/upgrading	Functional purity in modules	Rule
Recycleability	Material purity in modules	Rule

LEAD TIME IN DEVELOPMENT

Lead time in development will decrease when there is a possibility to work in parallel. In case studies, the decrease in development lead time due to the change from a part-by-part built product to a modular product was between 30–60% with a median of 45%.

To get complete development freedom, it is necessary for the interfaces between modules to be easy to specify and to remain fixed over a period of time. This results in minimal information flow between design groups and shortens the development time. Simple interfaces between the modules, without causing increased complexity within the modules, are preferable.

The specification of an interface is defined by gathering data on items such as form, fixation principles, number of contact surfaces and attachments, number of energy connection points, material flow, and signals. A certain amount of information is needed for every interface. Low complexity is, in this case, synonymous with ease to specify (low information content).

Boothroyd and Dewhurst have studied assembly difficulties in great detail, using the geometrical features of parts as the base. In their *Product Design for Assembly Handbook*, metrics for "assemblability" are given. These metrics can be used to calculate the interface complexity, which is, consequently, also a measure of the possibility for parallel product development.

When symmetry, thickness, size, etc., are ideal, handling difficulties and obstructed insertion operations do not exist, resulting in the shortest possible assembly operation time. An interface with such an ideal design will be simple to specify and, hypothetically, through a design for assembly (DFA) analysis on the module level, a direct value can be obtained relating to the possibility of work on parallel design projects. This value is called the *interface com-*

plexity, and is calculated as follows (the value is normalized by assuming the time for an ideal assembly operation is 3 seconds):

$$I_c = \frac{\sum_{i=1}^{N_m-1} T_i}{A_T} \qquad \text{(A-1)}$$

where

I_c = interface complexity

N_m = number of modules in one product variant

T_i = assembly time for one interface

A_T = ideal assembly operation time (3 seconds)

The probability of successful parallel development with minimal information flow needs between design projects increases when the value of the interface complexity is low. An ideal value of the interface complexity is reached when the ideal values for all the interfaces in the product are obtained. That is, when only one contact surface between each module is needed and "best practice" (10 seconds) for the interface assembly operation is reached.

$$I_{ic} = \frac{(N_m-1)10}{3} \qquad \text{(A-2)}$$

where

I_{ic} = ideal interface complexity

DEVELOPMENT COSTS

The number of carryover modules has a great influence on the development cost. As discussed earlier, a *carryover* is a part of a product (a module) that is carried over to the next generation of the product without any changes. The share of carryover modules directly influences development costs and can be used to evaluate different concepts when development costs are vital.

Holmes describes how the Xerox Corporation focuses on reuse in product development with the help of their reusability matrix (see Figure A-1) (Holmes 1993). This matrix is used together with quality function deployment (QFD) matrices, in which the customer needs and wishes are evaluated against existing products, modules, subsystems, and piece parts.

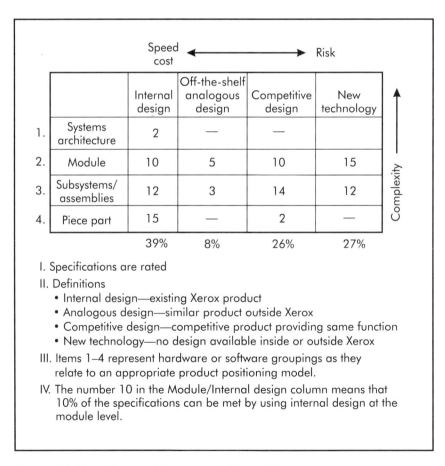

		Internal design	Off-the-shelf analogous design	Competitive design	New technology
1.	Systems architecture	2	—	—	
2.	Module	10	5	10	15
3.	Subsystems/ assemblies	12	3	14	12
4.	Piece part	15	—	2	—
		39%	8%	26%	27%

I. Specifications are rated

II. Definitions
- Internal design—existing Xerox product
- Analogous design—similar product outside Xerox
- Competitive design—competitive product providing same function
- New technology—no design available inside or outside Xerox

III. Items 1–4 represent hardware or software groupings as they relate to an appropriate product positioning model.

IV. The number 10 in the Module/Internal design column means that 10% of the specifications can be met by using internal design at the module level.

Figure A-1. Xerox Corporation's reusability matrix.

DEVELOPMENT CAPACITY

The demand for development capacity can be moderated with the help of black-box engineering. This means that the supplier, apart from the manufacturer, is also responsible for the development of a complete module. The discussions later in this appendix concerning systems costs may affect the decision about whether to use in-house or external development. The following questions should be asked:

- Are there strategic reasons why the technology should be kept in-house?
- Have we today and in the future enough resources to develop and produce this module?
- Is there any vendor offering the subsystem as a standard module today?

Once these questions are answered and the amount of black-box engineering has been decided, the development capacity can be measured by means of the share of purchased modules.

Mercer studied the possible savings and the key elements of modular supply in the automotive industry (Mercer 1995). In examining the potential savings from the modular out-sourcing of nine modules, a European volume manufacturer projected an average savings over the life cycle of the modules to be 40% in ongoing expense reduction. In addition, the manufacturer avoided other expenses, capital expenditures, and product and process redesign.

The conclusion from the study is that modular supply offers many opportunities and challenges for manufacturers and suppliers, and the growth of modular supply will continue. However, the planning of modular supply is found to be complex and variable, and the study offers no particular advice. Mercer concludes: "Confusion over exactly what and why a module is, is a sure recipe for failure and loss, one way or the other. Thinking through the module's value in a detailed and complete way is one means toward avoiding such adverse commercial outcomes."

A simple, structured four-step approach for the assessment of modular out-sourcing is outlined in Figure A-2.

1. Right modules	3. Right suppliers
• Technical feasibility • Substantial savings potential • Strategically neutral • Consequences controllable	• Preselection based upon capabilities and commitment • Final decision based upon alternative bids
2. Right integration	4. Right costs
• Early and tight integration of the selected supplier in the product development process	• Comparison and elimination of all direct and indirect costs

Figure A-2. Key elements to consider when planning to out-source modules (Mercer 1995).

PRODUCT COSTS

Direct material and labor are important components of production costs. Experience from earlier research shows that the detailed design of each module has a great influence on the product cost. Therefore, it is important to use proper design for manufacture and assembly (DFMA) principles when designing each module.

It might be expected that direct material costs would increase for modular products because of the eventual need for extra interfaces. However, case studies have shown that this is not necessarily the case. Companies have succeeded in controlling the risk of increased material costs, and the measured effect on the material costs is between an increase of 3% and a decrease of 10%, with a median of 6% decrease.

The product cost includes the module-specific capital costs, tools, fixtures, etc. The amount of these costs depends mainly on the number of articles, number of modules, and the complexity of the module assortment. The control of these costs on the assortment level is made possible by the greatest reuse of modules in the assortment and/or the reuse of processes.

The goal should be an assortment with the least variation of modules and interfaces that satisfy customer requirements. In other words, the complexity of the assortment should be minimized.

Pugh has used a measure calculated on the component level to determine the complexity of a product (Pugh 1991). If a complete modular product assortment is approached the same way as Pugh approaches a single product, it is possible to calculate the assortment complexity as:

$$A_c = \sqrt[3]{N_m N_{mt} N_c} \qquad \text{(A-3)}$$

where

A_c = assortment complexity

N_m = number of modules in one average product variant

N_{mt} = total number of module variants needed to build up the product range

N_c = number of contact surfaces between modules in one product

This equation shows that the complexity in a modular product assortment increases with:

- the number of modules in each product variant;
- the total number of module variants needed to build all product variants; and
- the number of contact surfaces in the interfaces.

The number of contact surfaces might be difficult to estimate or calculate. Experience has shown that the total assembly operation time (seconds) for the interfaces can be used as the basis for an approximation.

A modular concept that has the lowest value for the assortment complexity will have the lowest product costs amortized over the entire assortment. This is a measure that is impossible to obtain from a standard cost calculation.

According to Boothroyd and Dewhurst, an ideal assembly operation takes 3 seconds to perform. This value reflects a case in which the number of contact surfaces are as few as possible. If the total expected final assembly time is divided by the ideal assembly time, an approximation for the number of contact surfaces between the modules can be obtained.

$$N_c = \frac{\sum_{i=1}^{N_m-1} T_i}{A_T} \qquad \text{(A-4)}$$

where

N_c = number of contact surfaces between modules

N_m = number of modules in one product variant

T_i = expected assembly operation time for one interface

A_T = ideal assembly operation time (3 seconds)

Equation A-3, which calculates the assortment complexity, now becomes:

$$A_c = \sqrt[3]{N_m N_{mt} \frac{\sum_{i=1}^{N_m-1} T_i}{A_T}} \qquad \text{(A-5)}$$

where

A_c = assortment complexity

N_m = number of modules in one product variant

N_{mt} = total number of module variants needed to build up the product range

T_i = expected assembly operation time for one interface

A_T = ideal assembly operation time (3 seconds)

A precise calculation of the final assembly time (assembly of interfaces) can be obtained through a DFA analysis, which looks at the modules as components (Boothroyd and Dewhurst). This only pertains to the interface assembly. If the detailed knowledge at this stage does not make a DFA analysis possible, an approximation can be made based on an assessment of the difficulties in the final assembly (interfaces). Often, the relative difficulty of the interface assembly and piece-part assembly can be estimated at an early stage too, which has been shown in several cases. Generally, the number of assembly operations between modules equals the number of modules minus one, because one of the modules often serves as the base for the rest of the assembly operations. The approximation is:

$$\sum_{i=1}^{N_m-1} T_i = (N_m - 1)T_i \qquad \text{(A-6)}$$

where

$(N_m - 1)$ = Number of final assembly operations (interfaces) between modules

T_i = average assembly time for one interface (final assembly)

Does a best possible value for the assortment complexity exist? An ideal modular concept is one in which all the product variants needed can be built up by the combination of the same modules in different ways. Thus, there is no need for module variants other than those existing in one product variant, that is, $N_m = N_{mt}$. If the product is successfully divided into an ideal number of modules (see the "Lead Time in Assembly" section), it follows that:

$$N_m = N_{mt} = \sqrt{N_p} \qquad \text{(A-7)}$$

which gives

$$A_{ci} = \sqrt[3]{\sqrt{N_p}\sqrt{N_p}(\sqrt{N_p} - 1)T_i / 3} \qquad \text{(A-8)}$$

and when $T_i = 10$ seconds ("best practice") an approximation will be

$$A_{ci} = 1.5\sqrt{N_p} \qquad \text{(A-9)}$$

where

N_m = number of modules in one average product variant

N_{mt} = total number of module variants needed to build up the product range

A_{ci} = ideal assortment complexity

N_p = number of parts in complete product (see "Lead Time in Assembly" section)

T_i = average assembly time for one interface (final assembly)

SYSTEM COSTS

System costs are the total costs that arise for the support of the assembly system. These include items such as purchase costs, costs for production planning, quality control costs, production engineering costs, and logistics costs. The influences affecting each are outlined in Table A-2.

System costs are affected by whether or not a company chooses to manufacture or out-source product modules. If all modules are produced in-house, the highest likely system costs will occur; if all modules are procured from vendors, the lowest likely system costs will be realized. Simply put, the system costs are inversely dependent on the share of purchased modules.

Table A-2. Influences affecting system costs

Type of costs	Influenced by
Purchase	Number of vendors/number of different parts
Production planning	Complexity/number of parts
Quality control	Complexity/number of parts
Production engineering	Number of modules/complexity
Logistics	Number of vendors/number of parts/ number of different parts

The make or buy decision has been discussed by many authors. Venkatesan, for example, has studied the issues of strategic sourcing within the Cummins Engine Company in Columbus, Indiana (Venkatesan 1992). This case study, concerning the out-sourcing of pistons, reveals many interesting aspects of how make or buy decisions are normally made and how they should be made. From these experiences, the author defines a strategic sourcing process to follow when deciding whether or not to produce modules in-house.

The basis for the decision process is what is called the "architectural knowledge." *Architectural knowledge* is defined as the ability to capture customer needs and translate them into the performance specifications of subsystems. These findings are in line with the arguments of Fine and Whitney who have found that the skill to create a good specification and a good decomposition can be considered a core competency of a manufacturing company (Fine and Whitney 1996). It does not matter whether the suppliers are members of the customer company or not. Competency must exist in the ability to: write clear and complete specifications for the needed capability; identify suppliers capable of delivering items that meet the specifications, or create and train suppliers capable of doing so; and to determine whether the supplier has indeed delivered items that meet the specifications.

LEAD TIME IN ASSEMBLY

Based on the assumption that each module is concurrently assembled with the others and delivered to the main assembly line where complete modules are assembled to each other (see Figure A-3), an ideal value for lead time can be calculated. The ideal value assumes that there are no delays in assembly startup between the modules.

$$L = \frac{N_p T_A}{N_m} + T_t + (N_m - 1)T_i \qquad \text{(A-10)}$$

where

L = lead time

N_p = number of parts in complete product

N_m = number of modules in one average product variant

T_A = average assembly time for one part (10 seconds is "best practice")

T_t = average time for functional testing of modules

T_i = average final assembly time for interfaces between modules

This equation has a theoretical minimum value that can be calculated as:

$$\frac{dL}{dN_m} = -\frac{N_p T_A}{(N_m)^2} + T_i \text{ which is 0 when: } N_m = \sqrt{\frac{N_p T_A}{T_i}} \quad \text{(A-11)}$$

where

d = derivative, differential coefficient

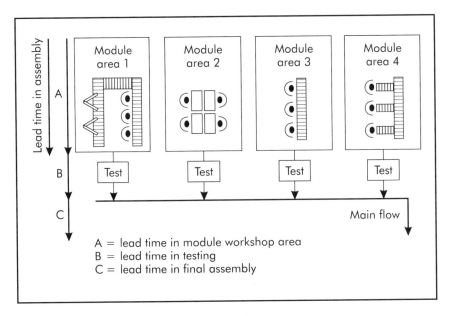

Figure A-3. Concurrent assembly of modules.

Experience has shown that the average "best practice" assembly operation time for parts is about 10 seconds (T_A) and an average final assembly operation for all modules in a product varies between 10 and 50 seconds, $T_A \leq T_i \geq 5$ T_A. If the average final assembly time (interface) is equal to the average assembly time for parts, the theoretical minimum of the lead time arises when:

$$N_m = \sqrt{N_p} \text{ (see Equation A-9)}$$

Together with Equation A-10, this yields a theoretical minimum lead time of

$$20\sqrt{N_p} - 10 \text{ seconds,}$$

not considering time spent on functional testing.

When the average final assembly time is longer than the average assembly time for parts, the ideal number of modules will decrease. In practice, the shortest lead time occurs when the number of modules is between

$$0.5\sqrt{N_p} \text{ and } \sqrt{N_p}$$

The lower value is valid when the interface assembly takes 5 times the time taken for the assembly of one part. A target value for N_p can be estimated at 60–70% of the part count in an old generation of the product. This is supported by experiences from numerous DFA analyses.

At an early stage, the values can be used as rules of thumb for targeting the number of modules in those cases where lead time is important. The lead time in assembly represents up to 40% of the total customer order lead time, indicating that assembly-oriented product structuring is generally important (Eversheim et al. 1996).

In Figure A-4, the ideal/minimum values are plotted as the number of parts in products, showing the relationship between interface assembly and part assembly times. The number of parts/assemblies can be used to estimate the targeted number of modules for the division of the product into modules.

Theoretically, it will be possible to shorten the lead time further by dividing each module into submodules. There is, however, a lowest possible limit for subdividing. That is when the work content in a module gets too small and further dividing into submodules is not justified from the assembly point of view, but might well be from other points of view.

In case studies, the total assembly lead time was measured and found to decrease by 10–73%, with a median value of 54%, when the assembly system was changed to accommodate modularization. The discussions here do not consider any balancing, handling, and system losses, which normally would increase the theoretical lead time considerably (Ellegård et al. 1992). However, using the concept

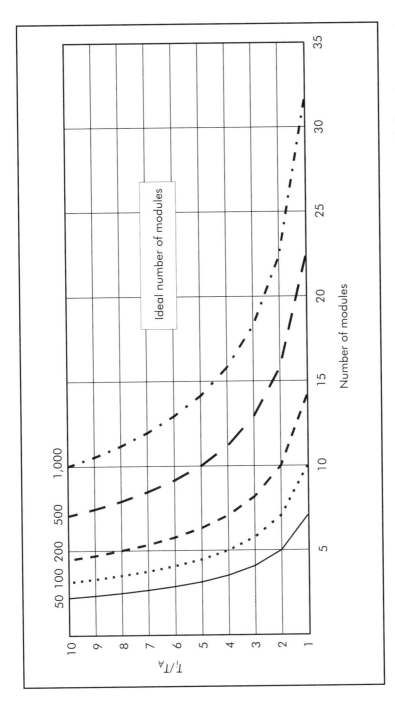

Figure A-4. Chart showing an estimation of the ideal number of modules. T_A = average assembly time for one part, T_i = average assembly time on final assembly line for one module interface. The curves represent different numbers of parts (50, 100, etc.) in the completed product.

of "small factories within the factory" will minimize the losses. Balancing and handling losses are cycle-time dependent and system loss is dependent on the number of assembly stations in a line. An assembly line adapted for modularization of the product will increase the possibilities to lengthen the cycle time as well as decrease the number of stations in one line, resulting in minimization of losses to the lowest possible level.

QUALITY

Quality in the assembly system will be improved when modules are designed to allow for separate functional testing. Only perfect modules should be delivered to the main flow. The increase in quality will be possible due to the shorter feedback time of fault reports within the module assembly lines (team work areas). As found in one example, it is ten times as expensive to repair a defect in an automotive front-wheel-drive brake unit after it is fully assembled than it is to repair the same defect at the point at which it occurs (Robinson et al. 1990).

Four circumstances encourage testing at the module level (Nevins and Whitney 1989):

- Tests might address faults that often occur.
- Testing might address faults that are substantially cheaper to diagnose or repair at the module level than later.
- Later tests for a fault may not be possible, because, for instance, the test points are no longer accessible.
- A specific test may not be available later; that is, later tests may reveal the fault in question only in combination with other faults, requiring additional tests or diagnoses.

The best possible quality, according to these criteria, will occur when all modules are separately tested. A modular product with the highest share of separately tested modules is best. In case studies, the separate testing of modules decreased the amount of rework by 37–75%, with a median of 56%.

In addition to assembly errors and part interferences caused by dimensional variations, parts may have defects not associated with the interfaces, such as material defects. Since these defects will not be influenced by the assembly system, they will not be dealt with further here.

Given that tolerance variation and assembly errors are independent variables with little likelihood of occurrence, the probability of a defect-free assembly can be found (Barkan 1992):

$$P_A = \prod_{i=1}^{n}\left[1 - C_k(T_i - A_T)^k\right](1 - D_p) \qquad \text{(A-12)}$$

where

P_A = probability that the total assembly is defect-free

n = number of assembly operations

C_k = a constant related to the quality control of the assembly operation

T_i = time required to complete one interface assembly operation

A_T = ideal assembly time (3 seconds)

k = exponent relating defect sensitivity to the assembly operation time

D_P = probability that the assembly contains a defect

Equation A-12 also reveals fundamental factors that can influence assembly defects:

- the number of defects in parts (D_P);
- part count ($i \approx n$; in most cases, the number of assembly operations equals the part count);

- the number of assembly operations (n);
- the complexity of the assembly operation measured as the divergence from the ideal assembly time ($T_i - A_T$); and
- quality control—the ability to perform an assembly operation without adding a defect (C_k).

A modular assembly, in which some or all modules are separately tested, contributes directly to the assembly defects, and Equation A-12 becomes:

$$P_{At} = \left[1 - C_k(T_i - A_T)^k\right]^{N_m - 1}\left[1 - C_k(T_A - A_T)^k\right]^{N_n} \quad \text{(A-13)}$$

where

P_{At} = probability that the total assembly is defect-free if some of the modules are tested

C_k = a constant related to the quality control of the assembly operation

T_i = average final assembly time for interfaces between modules

k = exponent relating defect sensitivity to the assembly operation time

N_m = number of modules

T_A = average assembly time

N_n = number of modules not tested

and

$$N_n = N_p - \sqrt{N_p \frac{T_i}{T_A} N_t} \quad \text{(A-14)}$$

(corresponds to the sum of parts in modules that are not tested)

where

N_p = number of parts in complete product

N_t = number of modules separately tested

As before, this transformation assumes that the ideal number of modules is reached and a tested module is defect-free.

According to published data (Barkan 1992; Brannan 1991), C_k varies between 1.2e-4 and 2.6e-4, and an ideal value for k will be 1. The values $C_k = 1.2\text{e-}4$ and $k = 1$ are used in further calculations. Research has also shown that an average assembly operation, T_n = 10 seconds, and an average interface assembly operation vary, $T_A \leq T_i \geq 5T_A$.

The quality improvements that can be realized by separate testing of some or all modules can now be calculated. The result of such a calculation is plotted in Figure A-5. The interpretation of the diagram is that there is "more to earn" for a product containing many parts than for a product with fewer parts. As reported in the case studies, Scania showed a quality improvement of 75% and Geotronics an improvement of 37% (Östgren 1994). As a truck contains a much higher number of parts than an instrument from Geotronics, this might indicate that the diagram shows an adequate picture.

 **VARIANT FLEXIBILITY**

The multiple use of modules, processes, and organizations is important when judging how a modular concept supports the creation of variants. A simple measure of the variant flexibility can be derived from the relation between the number of product variants and the total number of modules needed:

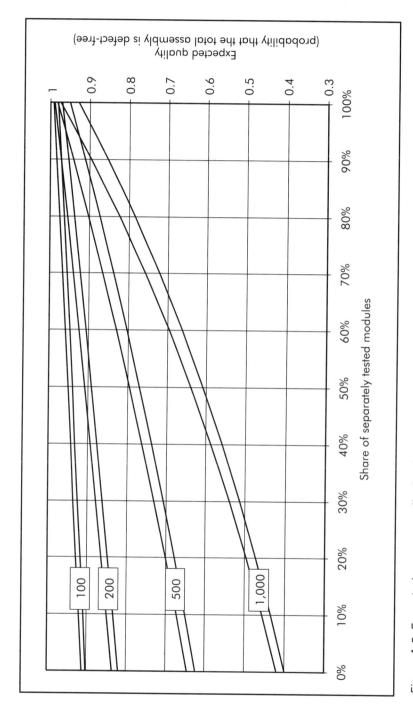

Figure A-5. Expected average quality (probability that the entire assembly is defect-free) with separate testing of modules. The curves represent the different numbers of parts in the completed product.

126

$$E_v = \frac{N_v}{N_{mt}} \qquad \text{(A-15)}$$

where

E_v = total number of modules needed

N_v = number of product variants (required by customers)

N_{mt} = total number of modules required to build up all the product variants

A high value indicates high similarity between product variants, which has many advantages, including fewer setups, fewer tools, and simpler order planning. For example:

- The well-known Nippondenso panel meter can be assembled into 288 variants from 16 total modules, and has an E_v of 18.
- Nippondenso's alternator family embodies 700 variants, is built from 46 total modules , and has an E_v of 15.2 (Kamath and Liker 1994).
- The Sepson modular mobile winch can be built in 28 variants out of 10 total modules, and has an E_v of 2.8 (Erixon et al. 1994).

In variant design, it is important to avoid unnecessary variants. "Variety in and of itself is not customization—and it can be dangerously expensive" (Pine et al. 1993). There is a distinction between strategic and tactical variety (Martin and Ishii 1996). *Strategic variety*, or what is noticeable by the customer, is decided by the product manager and involves the interaction of marketing and product design. *Tactical variety*, or what is not obvious to the customer, involves the use of different parts or processes for the product. Decisions about tactical variety require close cooperation between product design and production.

A German study showed, among the products studied, that 60% of newly developed variants already existed in earlier generations of the products. This study also concluded some questions to be asked during variant design:

- Will this really be a variant?
- How significant is it to the customer?
- Will it be clear to the customer that it is a variant?
- Where in the production chain will the variant appear?
- Which variants are necessary?
- In which part of the product can variants be allowed?

By asking these questions, the significance of creating variants is revealed, making it possible to control the variant explosion.

SERVICE/UPGRADING

To achieve easy interchangability of modules, it is vital that there are no functional interconnections between modules. For this reason, no single subfunction should be divided between two or more modules. By the use of the Module Indication Matrix™ (MIM™) this is probably already secured, but a check backward, at this stage, is recommended. A relevant check can be performed through the use of a design matrix (Suh 1990).

RECYCLEABILITY

To ensure a high degree of recycleability, the number of different materials should be kept as low as possible within each module. A simple Pareto chart (Ishikawa 1988) may give a picture of how this requirement is met, and the 80/20 rule can be used to set goals.

SUMMARY

The evaluation of concepts is summarized in the evaluation chart shown in Figure A-6. This chart serves as a checklist for the product characteristics that influence a good modular design. The relative importance of the requirements must be set in every case to estimate the yield.

Module Evaluation Chart			
Guide	Ideal, optimum or goal	Actual	Yield,%
General Number of parts in average product (N_p). A relevant objective for a new concept is 70%. (New N_p = 0.7 × Old N_p).	$N_p =$ _____		
Estimate the average assembly time relation between the part assembly operation and interface assembly operation. Common average part assembly is 10 seconds $(T_A = 10)$. 10 seconds operation time is an easy interface and 50 seconds a fairly difficult one $(T_A \le T_i \ge 5\,T_A)$. T_i = average assembly time for one interface T_A = average assembly time for one part (10 seconds)	Assembly time relation: $T_i/T_A =$ _____		
Lead time in assembly $L = \dfrac{N_p T_A}{N_m} + T_t + (N_m - 1)T_i$ where: L = lead time, N_m = number of modules in one product, T_t = average time for functional testing of modules	$20\sqrt{N_p} - 10 =$ _____ Ideal when assembly time relation = 1		
System costs Share of purchased modules in one product.	Goal = _____		
Product costs $A_c = \sqrt[3]{N_m N_{mt} \times \dfrac{\sum\limits_{i=1}^{N_m-1} T_i}{A_T}}$ where: A_c = assortment complexity, N_{mt} = total number of modules required to build all product variants, A_T = ideal assembly operation time	$A_{ci} = 1.5\sqrt{N_p} =$ _____		

Figure A-6. Module evaluation chart.

Module Evaluation Chart			
Guide	Ideal, optimum or goal	Actual	Yield,%
Quality Estimate the expected quality (probability for defect-free assembly) $P_{At} = \left[1 - C_k(T_i - 3)^k\right]^{N_m - 1} \times$ $\left[1 - C_k(T_A - 3)^k\right]^{N_n}$ where: P_{At} = probability that the total assembly is defect-free if some of the modules are tested, T_A = average assembly time, N_n = number of modules not tested and $N_n = N_p - \sqrt{N_p \dfrac{T_i}{T_A} N_t}$ (corresponds to the sum of parts in modules that are not tested) where: N_t = number of modules separately tested	$N_n = O$, why $P_{At} = \left[1 - C_k(T_i - 3)^k\right]^{N_m - 1}$		
Lead time in development $I_c = \dfrac{\sum\limits_{i=1}^{N_m - 1} T_i}{A_T}$ where: I_c = interface complexity, T_i = assembly time for interface (DFA)	$I_{ic} = \dfrac{(N_m - 1)10}{3} = \underline{\hspace{1cm}}$ where: I_{ic} = ideal interface complexity Observe N_m = the actual value for the concept evaluated		
Development costs Estimate the share of carryover modules following the rules	Goal = _____		
Development capacity Share of purchased modules	Goal = _____		

Figure A-6. (continued).

Module Evaluation Chart			
Guide	Ideal, optimum or goal	Actual	Yield,%
Variant Flexibility Product variants as: $$E_v = \frac{N_v}{N_{mt}}$$ where: N_v = number of variants that can be built, N_{mt} = total number of modules needed	Maximize		
Service/upgrading Check the MIM for functional purity.	No functional connections between modules		
Recycleability See separate Pareto chart (Ishikawa 1988)			

Figure A-6. (continued).

Appendix B: Glossary

Integration

The union (grouping) of technical solutions/components, based on the Module Drivers'™ markings in the Module Indication Matrix™ (MIM™).

Interface

The interaction/relation/contact between modules, which can be defined as: physical, energy transmitting, information (for example, geometry, electrical signals, or parameters), etc.

Interface Matrix

A detailed matrix within the Modular Function Deployment™ (MFD™) method used to specify and visualize interface relationships between modules.

Modularization

Decomposition of a product into building blocks (modules) with specified interfaces, driven by company-specific strategies.

Module

See **Modularization**.

Module Drivers™	Driving forces that indicate a subsystem/technical solution/component should form a separate module. These are the criteria (drivers) used to define modules.
Module Driver Profile	Horizontal sum of the Module Drivers in the MIM, reflecting the company's product strategy.
Module Specification	A summary specification for a module containing information about technical solutions, interfacing modules, types of interfaces, target values, quality parameters, etc.
Platform Plan	A description of the stepwise development the modules within a product platform should undergo within a foreseeable future.
Primary Development	Development of new, unknown technology.
Product Development	Development of known technology with in-house knowledge or in-house control.
Product Platform	The complete set of modules that can be combined and configured into a number of product variants in line with company strategy.
Pugh Matrix	A matrix used within the MFD method for the evaluation of alternative technical solutions.

134

Subassembly

Part of a product assembled into a unit to ease further machining or assembly.

Technical Solution

Selected component/system, or concept thereof, fulfilling a desired function (that is, a function carrier).

ABBREVIATIONS

DFA

Design for assembly—a method for systematic reduction of parts and assembly time.

MFD™

Modular Function Deployment™—a structured, company-supportive method with the objective of finding the optimal modular product design, considering the company's specific needs.

MIM™

Module Indication Matrix™—a matrix within the MFD™ method for the evaluation of the technical solutions with regard to the Module Drivers™.

QFD

Quality function deployment—a method used to interpret customer demands and translate them into product attributes (properties).

References

Barkan, P. 1992. "Benefits and Limitations of Structured Methodologies in Product Design." ME 217 A 92/93.

Boothroyd, G. and Dewhurst, P. 1994. *Product Design for Manufacture and Assembly*. New York: Marcel Dekker.

Boothroyd, G. and Dewhurst, P. 1987. *Product Design for Assembly Handbook*. Wakefield, RI: Boothroyd Dewhurst, Inc.

Brannan, B. 1991. "Six Sigma Quality and DFA—DFMA Case Study/Motorola, Inc." Boothroyd Dewhurst, Inc. *DFMA Insight,* Vol. 2, Winter.

Charney, C. 1991. *Time to Market: Reducing Product Lead Time*. Dearborn, MI: Society of Manufacturing Engineers (SME).

Ellegård, K., Engström, T., Johansson, B., Nilsson, L., and Medbo, L. 1992. "Reflective Production—Industrial Activity in Change," in Swedish. Gothenburg, Sweden: AB Volvo Media.

Erixon, G., Erlandsson, A., Yxkull, Av, Östgren, B. Mo. 1994. "Modularize Your Product," in Swedish. *Industrilitteratur*.

Erixon, G., Fredrikson, J., Romson, L., and Yxkull, Av. 1996. "Modularization in Practice," in Swedish. *Industrilitteratur*.

Erixon, G. 1998. "Modular Function Deployment—A Method for Product Modularization." Doctoral Thesis. Stockholm, Sweden: The Royal Institute of Technology.

Eversheim, et al. 1996. "Managing Multiple Product Variants in Assembly Control with a Fuzzy Petrinet Approach." Como, Italy: CIRP General Assembly.

Fine, C.H. and Whitney, D.E. 1996. "Is Make-buy Decision Process a Core Competence?" Cambridge, MA: MIT Center for Technology, Policy, and Industrial Development, February.

Holmes, B. 1993. "Competing on Delivery." *Manufacturing Breakthrough*, IFS, Jan./Feb.

Ishikawa, K. 1988. *Guide to Quality Control*. Methuen, MA: GOAL/QPC.

Kamath, R.R. and Liker, J.K. 1994. "A Second Look at Japanese Product Development." *Harvard Business Review*, Nov./Dec.

Martin, M.V. and Ishii, K. 1996. "Design for Variety: A Methodology for Understanding the Costs of Product Profileration." Irvine, CA: The 1996 ASME Design Engineering Technical Conferences and Computers in Engineering Conference, August 18–22.

Mercer, G. 1995. "Modular Supply in the 1990s: The Keys to Success." Chapter 11. *Europe's Automotive Components Business*, 2nd quarter.

Nevins, J.L. and Whitney, D.E. 1989. *Concurrent Design of Products and Processes*. New York: McGraw-Hill Publishing Company.

Östgren, B. 1994. "Modularization of the Product gives Effects in the Entire Production." Licentiate Thesis. Stockholm, Sweden: The Royal Institute of Technology, Department of Manufacturing Systems. TRITA-TSM R-94-2.

Pine, et al. 1993. "Making Mass Customization Work." *Harvard Business Review*, Sept./Oct.

Pugh, S. 1991. *Total Design: Integrated Methods for Successful Product Engineering*. Reading, MA: Addison-Wesley Publishing Company.

Robinson, L.W., McClain, J.O., and Thomas, L.J. 1990. "The Good, the Bad, and the Ugly: Quality on an Assembly Line." *International Journal of Production Research*, Vol. 28, No 5: 963-980.

Smith, P.G. and Reinertsen, D.G. 1991. *Developing Products in Half the Time*. New York: Van Nostrand Reinhold.

Suh, Nam P. 1990. *The Principles of Design*. New York: Oxford University Press.

Venkatesan, R. 1992. "Strategic Sourcing: To Make or not to Make." *Harvard Business Review*, Vol. 70, No 6. Nov./Dec.

Warnecke, H-J. 1993. *The Fractal Company: A Revolution in Corporate Culture*. Berlin, Heidelberg, New York: Springer Verlag.

Index

A

assembly, 37, 118-123
  concurrent, 119 (Figure A-3)
  defect-free, 123
  lead time in, 37 (Figure 4-6), 118-122
assortment complexity, 113
Atlas Copco Controls, 71-75

B

black-box engineering, 111

C

carryover, 20
common unit, 24
concept phase, 100-101
concurrent assembly, 119
costs,
  development, 109-110
  product, 112
  system, 116-117

D

defect-free assembly, 123
design, 13-14
  for manufacture and assembly (DFMA), 14
  scope, 13